Metamedicine^{SM}

Power and Medicine - The 21st Century Way

by
Vida C. Baron, M.D.

First Edition

ISBN 0-9624701-0-4

Published by   BAREZ Publishing Company
                    P.O. Box 23555-332
                    San Diego, CA 92123

Designed and printed by Windsor Associates

Printed in the United States of America

This book is dedicated to my father, Godson Ezekoli, a man ahead of his time; to Norman Baron and Dawn Baron who taught me unconditional love.

Table of Contents

Author's Note:

This book is intended as an introduction to a new idea in medicine. It is not a textbook on medicine and should not be used as such.

You would not perform surgery on yourself or anyone else by merely reading a book on surgery. Likewise, it is inadvisable to use the tools and methodology described in this book without proper training. The author and publisher assume no responsibility for any unauthorized uses of this book.

The clinical material presented in this work represents actual case histories. The identities of the patients and the specific circumstances have been changed to preserve patient confidentiality. The names used in this book are all fictitious and do not refer to anyone living or dead.

Prologue

"A wise man should consider that health is the greatest of human blessings, and learn how by his own thought to derive benefit from his illness."
- Hippocrates

The ideas contained in this book are new and yet they are as old as humanity itself. Like all knowledge, they always existed, waiting for the correct question or a series of "what ifs" for their revelation.

What if an illness is a much greater event than the misery we perceive it to be? What if an illness is actually a memorandum from one portion of ourselves to another, calling into conscious attention an obstruction in the path of our progress toward becoming more resourceful, more powerful and happier human beings? We are discovering that illness and disease are all these things and that within the information they contain is the key to unlocking full human self-expression. Healing of the illness becomes a by-product of the human evolution into a more successful being.

The discovery and resolution of what the disease is bringing to attention and the simultaneous symptomatic relief of the illness, result in a more advanced human being who has at once learned what he needed to know and freed himself from his illness.

As we enter the twenty-first century, I am fortunate to be among a new breed of doctor-healers who view disease within the larger scope of human consciousness and who have embraced the expanded role of medicine in human life.

In my lifetime, I have seen modern medicine accelerate from an emphasis on restoring diseased body parts to a greater focus on keeping the body healthy - i.e., preventive medicine. Now, with our society's recognition of health as a primary force in successful living, we are beginning to question the existence of disease and the role of illness in human lives.

What is disease and why is it necessary? The process of uncovering answers to this question has led us on a fascinating journey into the elements of the human personality construct, well beyond what we know as human anatomy. It has also led to the expansion of medicine into metamedicine and a new definition of health.

Metamedicine is traditional medical science practiced within the framework of the human consciousness factor. It is the art and science of modern medicine that reaches beyond simple survival of a disease. It is a view of disease as a tool for human growth and empowerment. The individual who goes through a disease process should emerge from it, an advanced human being. The patient is brought to see the function of the illness in his/her life. Thus, this enlightened patient is not really a "patient" in the traditional meaning of the word which implies submissiveness but an enlightened and empowered individual who takes matters into his/her own hands and takes an active role in making choices towards the solution of the disease. The result is amplification of the effectiveness of medical therapy in every way and a quantum leap forward in the individual's knowledge of himself.

This is a departure from the traditional medical practice where patients submit themselves to the physician, who then is expected to take over and restore them to good health. In metamedicine, the patient is allowed the lead. The physician stands beside him/her, educating and bringing technological aide as the patient walks the path of recovery to emerge as a more powerful human being. In other words, it is understood by all involved that the patient is in charge.

"And what is it that the people gain from their disease?" What they gain is as varied as the people and as numerous as the diseases they choose. People, as strange as it may seem, choose their diseases and it is fortunate that they do. We all do and you'll see how. Stories about human accomplishments following bouts with cancer and other illnesses abound in the literature. There is the little old lady who left her death bed to open schools for gifted children and the executive who after nearly dying of a perforated ulcer, now travels the world giving workshops on stress control. Each patient who encounters metamedicine has a fascinating story to share.

For as long as there has been recorded history, people have been fascinated by reports of control of mind over matter. Medical literature is rife with the placebo effect. This is a phenomenon where an inert substance or therapy in which a patient believes, cures him. But the same substance or therapy may not produce the same result in anyone else. Faith healing, naturopathy and other unusual cures have their following. However, medical science has never been comfortable with recognizing the validity of these phenomena and "cures", largely because they lack logical explanations, understanding and reproducibility.

Metamedicine provides a framework for that understanding and a spark of light to make comprehensible that great unknown territory—the human mind. Metamedicine is not a mysterious invention. It is a packaging of tools and knowledge in a way that serves special functions. I have been fortunate in coming by these tools and information through curiosity and sheer grace. I am deeply grateful for the inspirational ideas and contributions of many physicians before me; to Richard Bandler and John Grinder for providing us with neurolinguistic programming; to other civilizations for their love in freely sharing information and to Hippocrates, the father of medicine, for knowing all this at the beginning. This book is my act of passing along this gift to others.

1
Metamedicine in Action

The key to every man is his thought
Sturdy and defying though he look,
He has a helm which he obeys,
Which is the idea after which all his
    facts are classified.
He can only be reformed by showing him
A new idea which commands his own.
                              - Emerson.

The first act of a doctor and healer in metamedicine is to gain entrance into the patient's mind in order to see and understand his/her world. The way a person thinks or how a person internally represents experience is his/her viewpoint of the world or his/her map of the world. This concept is explored fully in later chapters of this work. For now, it is important to recognize that thought is the gate to the vast universe we know as the human mind.

In addition to the skills required to enter an individual's world, the metamedicine professional must have a working knowledge of the "self"—the personality or persona—because health and disease occur within the greater context of all aspects of the persona. Therefore, the first section of this work will focus on the elements of the personality construct. Knowledge of the human personality construct allows us to expand our concept of the human physiology to include the unique physiology of the mind-body interaction. It is within this greater vision of the human being that we can begin to perceive a new definition of health and disease.

Before exploring the foundational concepts of metamedicine, let us watch metamedicine in action in the following case report. The chapters that follow will explain some of the terminology and technology which may be foreign to you at this point but which is clearly illustrated below.

In the course of regular office hours one afternoon, Doctor Norman, a young general surgeon, glanced at the chart before entering an examination room to meet a new patient. Under the line titled "Chief Complaint," the nurse wrote simply "Upper abdominal pain, nausea and vomiting with bloody emesis." Doctor Norman took a deep breath, relaxed and entered the examining room to meet his patient, a 60-year-old local farmer named Elmer Wenzel. After introducing himself, he pulled up a chair, sat down opposite Elmer asking, "Say, how are things going at your farm?" He listened with interest as Elmer rattled on about how unpredictable and difficult it was to make a living on the farm. He was saying, "Even if you can grow a decent crop in spite of the weather and the pests, you never can tell about the market. Then there is the damned government...," and then Elmer paused, shook his head, visibly agitated. Doctor Norman cracked a joke about taxes and the government, and that broke the spell. Elmer laughed and Doctor Norman encouraged him to talk about the old times at the farm and relaxed back in his chair as if he had nothing else to do that day.

While Elmer chattered on, Doctor Norman paced his breathing, posture and body movements. He would ask Elmer questions now and again and took note of Elmer's eye accessing cues and language patterns. Gradually, Doctor Norman slowed his own respirations and observed that Elmer did the same. He then began leading Elmer in earnest and steered the conversation to the illness for which Elmer was there in the first place. Whenever he asked Elmer a question, he noticed that Elmer would look up and then cast his eyes toward the floor on the right side. Doctor Norman made a mental note of this. Later, he wrote on the chart under "Thought": Representational System "V-K". This means that Elmer saw images and then had a feeling about them. These images were either remembered images or constructed (made-up) images. Elmer told him that his stomach began bothering him a lot 18 months previously, "When things started looking hopeless." "From then on, everything just got worse," he concluded. He said he really didn't want to bother anybody about his illness. So he drank milk, avoided alcohol and took antacids.

"I am curious to know how you decided that it was time to come to see me," Doctor Norman said, getting up and walking towards the examining table.

"Well, after I had a third bout of throwing up and saw all that blood, I got worried. I told myself I ought to have this thing looked into." He looked down and his brow knotted up. Doctor Norman took a mental note of this and later recorded it in the chart under "Decision Strategy": V-K-A. This means that Elmer makes a decision by seeing images, getting a feeling about them and then telling himself what to do.

"And you got concerned that it may be something serious— like cancer?" Doctor Norman guessed, and Elmer nodded in agreement.

"Well, it is always best to look fear in the eye. This way it won't control us," Doctor Norman told him. "And once we see what it is, where it is, we can move in and rub it out." He smiled confidently and Elmer broke out into a broad grin. Dr. Norman reached out and squeezed his left shoulder .

He examined Elmer, ordered some laboratory tests and had no trouble at all getting Elmer to consent to a gastroduodenoscopy the next day. He said, "We need to take a look in there and see what's going on so we can get a handle on this problem."

When Elmer was ready to be taken home after his endoscopy, Doctor Norman encouraged him to relax and spend the next few days at the catfish pond on his farm. You see, during the initial visit, Doctor Norman found out that the thing Elmer enjoyed the most was

3

"piddling away time at the pond" as Elmer put it. Elmer's family had maintained a sizeable pond at the farm and had it stocked with catfish. Once in a while, the entire Wenzel clan would get together for a picnic at the pond and have a "fish fry". Although Elmer loved spending time at the pond and had toyed with the idea of developing a catfish business in it, he didn't feel good doing that. His parents didn't regard that as a man's proper job. They had insisted that any Wenzel male worth his salt must be able to make a living growing cotton. So, Elmer put any ideas about catfish farming out of his mind.

The pathology report came back negative for cancer, from the biopsy specimens that Doctor Norman had taken from Elmer's duodenal ulcer. He had Elmer and Mrs. Wenzel called in to see him at the office. Elmer and his wife were relieved that all Elmer had was a bleeding duodenal ulcer. Then Doctor Norman explored treatment of the condition with them.

"You can have surgery or conservative treatment with drugs. Both may relieve the condition but neither may heal you, Elmer," he told him. "Healing this disease depends entirely on you."

"Doctor, I believe what you said about stress. I know that I brought this illness on myself, what with all that worrying," Elmer submitted. "But what can I do to fix things?"

"I could put you in the hospital and we'll try drug therapy to see if the bleeding will stop. If it doesn't stop, we may have to consider surgery," Doctor Norman told him. The doctor looked at both of them, pulled at his chin and added, "But that will cost you a bundle, even if you have medical insurance, which you don't." The couple looked at each other sadly and stared at the floor.

"Then again, I could let you go home on drug therapy and see how that works," Doctor Norman continued and Mrs. Wenzel gave a sigh of relief. "There is a catch to that though," he continued. "You would have to let your sons mind the farm, because you are going to have to take it real easy for quite a while. Just so you don't get bored, I recommend you whip your catfish pond into shape. My family and I would be more than happy to pay you to fish there and have a picnic on the grounds. And when you see how well that works for you, how good that makes you feel, you will tell yourself that you did the right thing."

Elmer Wenzel's face lit up like the early morning sky. Doctor Norman gave him a prescription for Tagamet and diet recommendations and he couldn't wait to get out of the office. Before he left, Doctor Norman asked him to tell him again about the catfish picnics the Wenzel clan used to have, so he would know what to expect when he and his family get to the Wenzel farm for a picnic. As Elmer excitedly told what went on on those picnics, Doctor Norman touched his left shoulder repeatedly until Elmer couldn't stop laughing. Then, Dr. Norman said to him. "Every time you think about your farm from now on, you will feel this way," and Doctor Norman squeezed his left shoulder again. Elmer glowed. As he walked Elmer and his wife to the reception desk, he made a statement about cotton farming, and Elmer just smiled.

A few months later Elmer and his wife made a special visit to Doctor Norman. Elmer said that he had been off of the drug for quite some time and had never felt so good in his life.

"Yeah," his wife concurred, "he acts like he's seventeen years old again."

They told Doctor Norman that the catfish pond had blossomed into a wildly successful operation and they have had more ponds dug out and stocked with catfish. Families came from all over and paid to fish and picnic.

"And Elmer just loves to yap with folks all day long, "Mrs. Wenzel laughed. "And we've made so much money, we've already paid you in full Doctor."

"We can never pay you enough for what you've done for us Doc." Elmer's voice was shaking with emotion.

"Oh, you cured yourself," Doctor Norman said. "I just pointed you in the right direction, that's all. Just let others know what they can do for themselves."

"Oh, he is," Elmer's wife teased. "He is singing your praises to anyone who'll hold still long enough to listen. He calls you the world's greatest doctor."

And so a person and a life were healed and an illness cured. That is what metamedicine is all about. The true meaning of health was achieved here; Elmer Wenzel's life became happier and more productive than it was prior to his illness. It can be said that his disease served as the tool to get him onto the path that represents his true expression in life; the path wherein he is happiest in the service of his fellow men and is prospering doing so. A year later, when Doctor Norman was at a picnic at Elmer's catfish farm, Elmer intimated to him, "Doc, I can't believe I am getting paid doing this!"

Now let us take a look at what went on in this case study.

Dr. Norman focused initially on getting into the patient's world by achieving rapport. Whatever time this took, he considered an excellent investment because a lot depended on it. In actual fact, he did not spend an inordinate amount of time because it would have taken the same amount of time or more to ferret a useful medical history out of a suspicious and uncooperative patient anyway.

He put the information he gathered about Elmer's thought process to good use when he recommended that gastroduodeno-scopy—a moderately expensive diagnostic procedure—be done. He presented it in the language of Elmer's thinking process, "We need to take a look in there and see what is going on, so we can get a handle on this problem." This is what is regarded in Neurolinguis-tic Programming (NLP) to be a visual and kinesthetic presentation. Of course, Elmer bought it because that is how Elmer thinks. It was as if he was talking to himself. Had Doctor Norman not had this skill and used it but had instead said, like any ordinary surgeon would, "You need a gastroduodenoscopy for a proper diagnosis as soon as possible," Elmer would have probably stared at him, and then would have possibly told him that he needed time to think it over. Valuable time would have been wasted while Elmer mulled it over. He may have called the doctor's office to ask all kinds of questions to find out in every detail what gastroduodenoscopy entailed. As it was, NLP rapport technology circumvented all that and kept trust in the doctor-patient relationship.

Doctor Norman allowed his patient to take the responsibility for healing himself. He could have stuck Elmer into a hospital bed where he could visit him at his own convenience. The doctor would not only feel that this would be safe for Elmer but would be certain that this was the safest thing for himself, from a malpractice point of view, because he would be having everything documented to cover his own behind, just in case a law suit ensued. But, Doctor Norman was no ordinary doctor. He practices metamedicine and so he practices with integrity. All his actions in this doctor-patient relationship are focused on serving his patients' interests. He trusts his own power, instead of fearing that there may be something to protect himself from. He does not "play God" either, demanding that the patient accept whatever decisions he makes. Instead, he suggested several plans of action and allowed the patient to make choices. He also used his skills to assist the patient in arriving at the choice that would result in the most effective resolution of the disease.

With Elmer, it was clear that he loved the catfish pond more than growing cotton. But the ingrained belief that this was not a proper man's work had prevented him all along from doing this work that he loved. That was his real disease—a negative belief that denied him true self expression. Doctor Norman skillfully used Elmer's convincer strategy to nudge him into choosing the work he loved. He subtly went against the true culprit, negative belief. To do so, he had to elicit Elmer's decision making strategy asking Elmer how he decided to come to his office. Recall that Elmer had answered that having seen the third bloody emesis, he became concerned and he then told himself that he ought to go see Doctor Norman. His decision strategy here is visual-kinesthetic-auditory internal or V-K-A. So Doctor Norman presented Elmer with the most resourceful choice in this format. "And, when you see how well it works for you, how good it makes you feel, you can tell yourself that you're doing the right thing."

It was like Elmer himself voicing his own decision because this is how Elmer makes decisions. So, this choice clicked into place in Elmer's brain.

7

As Elmer began to succeed financially in the catfish business, as it was natural that he would, he replaced his old negative belief with a positive belief in making a living doing what he loved. This was the actual healing because it kicked his emotional energy towards his true signature vibratory frequency, and in this energy state, he was no longer a person who had ulcers.

Did Elmer then really need the peptic ulcer drugs? Maybe yes and maybe no. However, he came to Doctor Norman out of an ingrained belief system which has faith in modern medicine, including drugs and surgery. Therefore, use of the ulcer drugs can and did facilitate the resolution of his ulcers. Ultimately, any therapy works only if the patient believes in it to begin with. Without the change in belief resulting in change in lifestyle, could Elmer's peptic ulcer have healed? Yes, but the disease would have remained because the illness in his gastrointestinal tract occurred within a larger context involving a key issue in his life—his self expression. That particular ulcer would have healed but since nothing was truly resolved, he was liable to develop other ulcers or other illnesses in other body systems.

With the metamedicine approach, Doctor Norman went far beyond the usual mechanistic repairing of the gastrointestinal tract. He coached the man to a healing by nudging him into becoming his true self—the best possible human being he could be. In that state health, wealth and happiness flow easily to the man because he is in his optimum energy state of beingness.

Disease can provide you with profits greater in value than money once you recognize its purpose within the greater universe of human consciousness. In redefining disease from the viewpoint of a deeper understanding of the human mind, metamedicine goes beyond the scope of modern medicine by calling into action, during the healing process, the unique and incredible power that we all are as human beings.

The technology of modern medicine is focused on the goal of getting you well, getting you to recover from an illness. In order to achieve this goal, medical science has devised tools and methods to

8

study and reverse the physiological effects of disease. As doctors, we use our considerable skills and these tools to treat each patient in order to achieve a cure. We can describe in great detail the disease process and the healing process. But we know that in the end, it is the body that actually heals itself. We have therefore, always recognized that awesome force which heals the patient but have never had a context in which to describe it.

Most of us physicians have suspected for a long time that a human being is more than what we in medicine call a physical body. We sense that we are a complete energy unit, greater than the sum of our parts. The mobilization of this unique and powerful force that we are as human beings is the task of metamedicine. With the knowledge of the completeness of the unit of life force which we all are, metamedicine then asserts that individuals should emerge from a disease process more powerful than they were before they became ill. It further contends that the disease process was intented to do just that all along .

The claim that we are a complete unit of life force implies that we contain everything we can ever imagine and that we have the power to create any kind of life here on earth that we desire. This is because we have stored away in that vast and wondrous computer, the human mind, all of the elements for a successful and happy life. The trick is to know how to bring these resources out at the appropriate time in a way that serves us. Only a few of us have developed the ability to do this consciously. In order to grasp this idea, we must first understand what we are. Exactly what are we besides muscle, bones, organs and brains? Let us embark on a journey to find out; to map the unknown territory.

The answer is that *we are energy*. Fundamentally, everything is energy. Solid matter is a form of energy; so are liquids and the air we breathe. Everything in nature is energy in one form or another.

All matter, both solid and liquid is composed of molecules. Molecules are made up of atoms. An atom is made up of electrons circulating around a nucleus. This arrangement can be broken down into protons and neutrons and reduced further to quarks. Like little

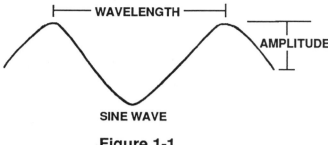

SINE WAVE

Figure 1-1

boys trying to find out what makes the watch tick, scientists broke open the quarks and found they were made of light. Light, like all other energy, has varying wave lengths.

From physics we learn that energy occurs as wave patterns. Essentially these waves are vibrations of certain amplitudes, wavelengths, and frequencies. They occur as excursions in equal and opposite directions around a zero or null line forming a sine wave (Fig. 1-1). Frequencies describe the number of wave lengths occurring per unit of time. As an example, take a look at the sine wave of sound or the waves of an electrical current. They are all described by their amplitudes, wave lengths and vibratory frequencies. Similar wave patterns be it objects of the same nature or a group of sound patterns may have the same amplitude but different frequencies or the same frequencies but different amplitudes .

The human body is matter. Since matter is made up of molecules which, in their basic form, are energy, it can be said that we are energy. We can describe the sum total of all the energies which we contain as our natural frequency or as our signature vibratory energy level. Examples of natural frequencies or core vibrations are abundant. As an example, each bridge has its own natural frequency. If a group of soldiers were to march across a bridge marching at cadence that had a frequency that corresponds to the bridge's natural frequency, this could amplify these vibrations to a point at which the bridge could disintegrate.

We human beings are self-aware forms of energy with the ability to change certain characteristics of this energy. We are subject to the same natural laws as all other energy. Energy cannot be created or destroyed. It can only be transformed from one form to another. Just as similar objects (similar wave patterns) are differentiated by their vibratory frequencies, so are human beings. Each human being's core frequency is his/her signature vibration. We will explore this further in the section on emotion which can be thought of as energy in motion or energy motion.

Energy exists infinitely. Thus, we, as self aware forms of energy, like all other energy, exist infinitely. That means that we always exist. We may undergo changes, but we never cease to exist. So how is it then that we die? Now, this book does not pretend to be a work on theology and it is in no way meant to challenge anyone's religious views. What is expressed here is intended only as a means of understanding a different way of looking at ourselves.

It is only the limited version of the totality of the self-aware being which we are, that dies. This limited version is what we recognize as our physiological selves.

"So," you ask, "if that is so, how come we don't know it?" The answer to that mystery is the key to understanding our lives here on earth.

11

"A man is a god in ruins."
 - Emerson

We are beings who play the game of forgetting. The capacity and willingness to forget is the vehicle for the creation of our limitations as human beings. This is really obvious when you come to think of it. We talk in terms of our subconscious and unconscious minds. We also speak in terms of parts of ourselves. We say, "A part of me feels this way or that way."

We have compartmentalized ourselves, and this has become the source of our limitations. From this idea of separation it is easy to see how we have carved up our minds into bins. To call some of these bins the conscious, subconscious, and unconscious mind is only a matter of sticking on the labels.

The unconscious and subconscious minds are those places we lock up or store portions of knowledge about ourselves which we don't want to be aware of, or to deal with. Once locked up in those compartments, we forget them. Then, like a child who fears walking into a dark closet, we resist exploring the contents of the subconscious and unconscious minds. As forgetting becomes complete, we plunge into the darkness of believing that all we are is the physical being that walks this earth. Without the knowledge of its full power, this physiological being invariably slides into ignorance and negativity.

Most people wonder why we would knowingly choose to become limited. I don't know the answer specifically. But taking a clue from nature, I would suspect that it is for the fun of it. Nature does not like boredom. An infinite being could create anything it is capable of creating. The saying goes like this: "What nature does not forbid, it demands." Even as limited beings, we continuously create everything we are capable of imagining. If you doubt it, think about all the magnificent and ingenious inventions we've created for warfare, and look at all the ways we've devised for destroying each other.

By the same token, it is beginning to occur to some of us that

12

we can choose to use the same creative force to infuse human life with health, wealth and happiness. In other words, we can choose to make limited beingness a positive experience. However, the suspicion persists that only a warped soul would consider limited beingness to begin with. Not exactly. Look at it this way: the game of falling into the darkness (forgetting) and working your way back to light (awakening) definitely adds richness to the experience of your total beingness. Notice that I call it a "game." If you doubt the validity of this statement, remember that children in just about every culture in the world play the game of hide and seek. And they enjoy it!

As beings of total freedom, we can choose how we can play out the game of going from forgetting to remembering; of going from darkness to light. And we do indeed choose our methods and our tools during our lifetimes.

At this point, I usually run into protests of "I certainly didn't choose to be ill," from my patients. They recoil as if I had just turned into a monster before their very eyes. I laugh, and then assure them that once they know how we function as personalities, a lot of things will become clear. Then they will know how to change the circumstances of their lives by changing themselves. And so will you.

2

The Metamed Model of Mind-Body Physiology (Metaphysiology)

Medical science has now begun to admit that there may be more to health and disease than mere bodily mechanical function. However, each study into the mind-body connection in disease states is still presented in an atmosphere suffused with skepticism. This skepticism is confused with objectivity which is mistakenly taken as a proper scientific atttude. Please note that objectivity is a valid scientific attitude. Skepticism on the other hand, is a personal judgement—a prejudice at best, which obscures objectivity. Nonetheless, the observation that there is a connection between disease, emotion, belief and thought is valid.

You will not find volumes of references or quotations from various scientific papers on these topics in this book because this work is not designed to prove anything to anybody. The ideas expressed in this work are a foundation for achieving health and enjoying more power in life. Every individual's body and life is his own laboratory. Test out the ideas presented here in your life. If they work for you, use them. If they do not work for you, then don't use them. What I do guarantee is that understanding and putting to useful advantage, the metamedicine model of the mind-body physiology will make you a more powerful human being.

The metamedicine model of the human mind-body physiology expands the scope of medical science. The root of the dissatisfactions of both the patient and the doctor with modern medicine can be traced directly to the limited focus of medicine on the physical body.

Medical education is based on the knowledge of human anatomy, the functioning or the physiology of the body and the effect of disease states on them. Based on this knowledge, we are then able to choose from a large medical armamentarium the best weapons against the disease.

The growth of the technical part of medicine has been so rapid and so exciting in the latter part of this century, that the concept of health is virtually limited to the mechanical aspects of body systems alone. The limited focus is to a large extent responsible for turning medical science into the science of body mechanics. Hence, doctors fall into the role of playing mechanics of body parts.

As my generation of doctors responds to the lure of medical technology, to specialize even more in body parts, we begin to recoil from the ramifications of our roles. We are waking up to the fact that what we have on our hands is a society of patients who literally dump their bodies on us to repair, refusing to take any responsibility for their health. Who is to blame? Nobody.

Medical technology is great, and it has served us all. I, as well as thousands of doctors worldwide, feel fortunate for the tools of this technology and have saved countless thousands of lives with them. As long as patients are treated as defective body parts with a brain somewhere, they will act with no self-empowerment, taking little or no responsibility for their health or disease. The total dependency, which is inevitably created, polarizes the doctor and the patient. The doctor finds the burden of taking full responsibility for fellow human beings onerous, and the patient begrudges his/her power-lessness. Then, what should have been an invigorating and satisfying relationship, quickly degenerates into a show of mutual distrust, with lawyers watching from the wings, ready to pounce.

We doctors feel this keenly; we complain to each other endlessly about how the medical profession is losing ground to the government, lawyers, and insurance companies. We seek solace from each other by venting our fears and complaints in the halls and lounges of our hospitals, to no avail. The patients who get the repair jobs feel a vague longing for the family doctor of yesteryear who, even though he/she couldn't do that much for their illnesses, maintained an intimate relationship with them. This doctor was more like a personal friend or a family member. What is to be done to remedy this situation?

We need to go back and redesign the basics. We need to expand our concept of the human physiology to include the consciousness factor. When we include consciousness in the human physiologic equation, everything changes. The practice of medicine becomes the practice of metamedicine.

Metamedicine imbues modern medical practice with more power. We, as doctors, begin to see and respect our patients as self-empowered beings and we approach disease with an intensified interest and curiosity. All individuals who now understand this expanded view of themselves will recognize their power of not only being capable of healing themselves but of utilizing disease for improving their lives.

Study the following illustration and metamedicine's new description of human physiologic anatomy that includes this consciousness factor, without judgement and without prejudice. Use it as a blueprint in the healing process, and watch miracles happen as I have. I will make no effort to describe the human gross or microscopic anatomy, as excellent books abound on these subjects. I will presuppose some degree of general knowledge in these areas in the following discussion of human physiology, anatomy, and disease. Medical details of these areas may distract from the essence of metamedicine which is what this work is about.

I have stated that everything in existence is energy in one form or another. Energy, like matter, cannot be created or destroyed. It can only be changed, transformed, or expressed in different ways. Human consciousness is a form of energy within all the energies of existence. As such, it can change or express itself in an infinite number of ways.

In this work, we are focusing only on the expression of human

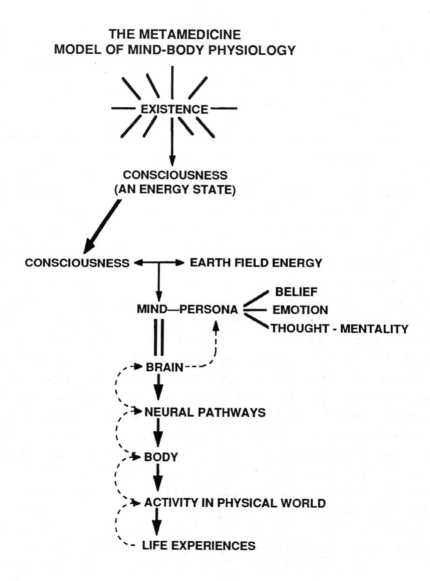

THE METAMEDICINE
MODEL OF MIND-BODY PHYSIOLOGY

EXISTENCE

CONSCIOUSNESS
(AN ENERGY STATE)

CONSCIOUSNESS ◄──► EARTH FIELD ENERGY

MIND—PERSONA ── BELIEF
EMOTION
THOUGHT - MENTALITY

BRAIN

NEURAL PATHWAYS

BODY

ACTIVITY IN PHYSICAL WORLD

LIFE EXPERIENCES

Figure 2-1

consciousness on our planet Earth—what we regard as our world or physical reality. In terms of the physical world or physical reality, human consciousness is expressed as the physical human form (body). In energy terms, it operates within the earth's energy field (electromagnetic medium) as the mind, which contains the three aspects of each persona or personality: thought, belief and emotion—which are integral parts of our nonphysical existence.

The physical organ through which the mind is expressed is the human brain. It is an electro-chemical-mechanical unit which controls the human body. As I have stated, detailed description of the body anatomy and the fascinating intricacy of its functioning are not within the scope of this work. The human body functions as the physical elements through which the mind interacts with the world. The various body systems: the vascular system, the digestive system, the neural system, the musculo-skeletal (locomotor) system, the hormonal system, etc., function and interact with each other in a way that allows the body as a whole to be a self-sustaining unit.

The human brain can be likened to a computer which receives input from the world around us through the various sense organs of the human body for the persona to process and act upon. It also sends output from the persona via the same route to the world and this is how we experience our physical lives.

The human body is run by the brain through neural pathways and neural hormonal mediators. All sensory organs in the body function to feed information (input) from the world environment into the brain. The brain must process this information before we can know or recognize what the information contains. Thus what we see, hear, feel, taste, and smell are the brain's interpretations of these outside symbols. The other organs and tissues of the body function as support systems for nutrition, directly or indirectly, and for reproduction .

The mind-body (nonphysical-physical) complex functions as a feedback loop for the human consciousness expressed as the persona. (See Figure 2-1 on page 18.)

In describing the electrical functioning of the brain, neuroscientists observed that each thought caused new electrical pathways to form between the cells of the brain. They state that the neural pathways, or what we may call the basic wiring of the brain (the blueprint of the circuit board), is governed by the belief systems. In other words, the brain is wired according to our beliefs. Each new thought will then make changes in this basic wiring system.

Scientists have observed that neuropeptides, which are the neurohormonal mediators of the various reactions in the brain and the body, are under the influence of emotion. Each belief activates an emotion which generates chemical activity in the appropriate neuropeptides, triggering an electrical event in the mechanical neural pathways to the end organs of the body.

To remove disease that is causing malfunction in the body's end organs, the rational thing to do would be to go directly to the circuit board (belief system) and fix things there by replacing the culprit parts.

Thought has been described as the aspect of the persona which focuses us to physical reality; in other words, our world. It is tantamount to our outer aware consciousness. It is the tool with which we bring into physical reality or experience whatever we have in our blueprints (beliefs). We also use it to change all aspects of the persona (what we are). Mentality (thought) has also been described as being the vehicle whereby the persona expresses its birthright of choice, which is free will, in the world. Please pause and let this last idea sink into every intelligent cell of your body, because the implication of this knowledge as it relates to health and disease is vital.

Mentality, or thought, is only one aspect of the persona consciousness and so its arena, which is our outer aware consciousness, is only a limited version of our totality. This means that there is a lot more of ourselves than what we are consciously aware of. One of the ways we become aware of these other levels of ourselves is by paying attention to what is happening in our physical life which includes our bodies. One of these powerful attention-getting devices is disease.

It is important to understand that the human mind and body are expressions of the same conscious energy. The body can be thought of as a physical extension of the mind. Conversely, the mind can be viewed as the nonphysical representation of the body.

The body functions to express physically that which is in the mind. Thought, through neural pathways, generates physical action in the body. The resulting activity in the body or of the body in the physical world creates changes which we experience subjectively as positive or negative. We interpret this feedback as pleasant or painful, as success or failure. The feedback mirrors the activity in the nonphysical persona. In other words, the brain puts out choices we have made. These are then reflected back to us as conscious experiences. These experiences are sensed emotionally as the consequences of the choices. The choices can then be changed or reinforced.

Since our outer aware consciousness is limited to the experience of our mentality in the physical world, we are quite often not fully aware or conscious of some of the choices we are making. Remember that mentality or thought is only one aspect of the total personality, and choices are made at all the other portions or levels of the personality, at the belief and emotional energy levels. These choices often remain outside of conscious awareness. Nevertheless, they are reflected by the actions of the physical body as experiences in the physical world.

Events or occurrences in the body are the results and the reflections of choices made in the persona. We may recognize these choices consciously, or they may remain outside of our conscious awareness, but they are our choices nonetheless. Does this mean that we choose health and prosperity as well as poverty and disease? The answer is an unqualified "yes!"

Now, please, before you begin protesting that there is no way you would choose disease or poverty, and before you accuse me of getting out of touch with reality, think of this. Having choices means that you are self-empowered to take on the responsibility of making other choices consciously—any and all choices including choices you prefer. All that is required for us to change any situation we don't prefer is that we *accept responsibility* for making all choices in what we experience. There are many methodologies and tools available for making the necessary changes in the choices we have made and their resulting physical effects. They range from simple rest and relaxation to complex surgery on the physical body level. On the mind level, it may range from changing a thought pattern to changing belief systems using skills like Neurolinguistic Programming (NLP) and hypnosis.

Let us take a look at the physiological changes which take place during a disease (Fig. 2-2).

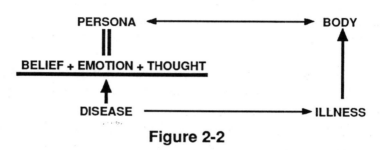

Figure 2-2

The way we usually perceive or experience a disease is as an illness. The illness may be a pain, a discomfort, or a malfunction of parts of the body. There are volumes of medical literature describing human pathology. For the sake of simplicity and brevity, I will get to the point with the following simple description of disease as an illness in the physical body.

The illness may be perceived by the brain as a threat to the life of the individual or at least as an undesirable feeling—a negative event. The drop in energy that we feel (the lows) and the fear and anxiety that accompany illness are what we generally term as a loss of the sense of well-being. These all correspond to or reflect a negative change in the emotionality (energy state) of the persona.

It may be this early noticeable change in the emotional energy during an illness that induced medical science to begin considering a mind-body link in disease. Peptides are being studied as the chemical basis for this connection. Whatever the nature of the linkage may be, the fact remains that we are beginning to recognize that an illness in the body signals a *dis*-ease state of mind and specifically in one or more aspects of the persona construct. It is more accurate to say that a disease in the persona is reflected as an illness in the body. The configuration or type of the disease specifies what the disease is all about at the mind level.

Can we cure the illness without eradicating the disease at the mind level? Yes, we can, and we do. This is what we do currently in medical practice and it is an excellent job of body mechanics. Is it important to eradicate the disease at the source—the mind? Absolutely. You see, if you do not remove the disease at its source, it will continue to manifest itself as other illnesses until it gets our conscious attention and compels us to change our choices, that is, until we achieve real *healing*. In the chapter on disease, I described the case of the young woman who continued to develop recurrent back disorders until she resolved and integrated the disease in her mind.

Recently, at our laser surgery clinic, I was asked to consult in the case of a priest who suffered from a fascinating array of skin tumors. Some of these were cancers that were scattered all over his body. He had had innumerable procedures for removal of the more disabling growths, and he just kept growing more crops of these tumors. After I introduced myself as an anesthesiologist, and gained access to his world, I asked him, "Do you want to stop making these tumors or would you rather have us keep playing with you this way—slicing up your body every few weeks?"

This man had some difficulty deciding to drop his "cross" (his name for his illness) because he felt it was a good tool in getting the attention of his congregation. I suggested that he might consider substituting "healing" as a better choice of a tool for approaching his congregation. If he could get excited about the idea, he could then proceed to make the necessary changes. This man consciously refused to part with his tumors. He stated that his disease was a service to medical science because he was being written up in

23

medical journals! And so his disease remained. This man, however, understood that in order to heal himself of his disease, he must and could make other choices of ways to serve humanity .

Where do we make these choices or changes? In the hierarchy of the persona construct, thought is the most superficial followed by emotions, with the most powerful, belief, being at the deepest level.

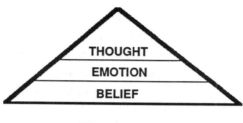

Figure 2-3

Changes made at the deepest level—the belief systems—are the most effective and the most permanent in bringing about healing of disease. Choice of the appropriate emotional energy provides the most potent energy climate for removal of the disease state. The correct mentality (thought) is what we must use in making these changes. The specific illness manifested in the body is a cue to what the disease is about. It is also a clue to where the problem lies as we will see in the section of this work describing disease.

Once the changes are made in the persona using other choices, a state of equilibrium—the zero rest point, if you will— is achieved. In this state, no disease can occur and the individual can continue to live along the path of his/her fullest expression of the self.

The persona, or personality, is that which determines the limited aspect of the total consciousness we experience in physical life. Recall that physicality—physical life—is nothing more than a certain vibrational frequency of the energy universe. The makeup of the personality is malleable, and this fact equips us with magical powers to create whatever we want. Before we delve into the actual methods of changing who we are, or what we fondly call "the change works," it is useful to explore the nature of thought, emotion and belief.

Again, remember that first there is consciousness energy which is the totality of what we are. Our physiological self is the filtered down version of this consciousness through the prism of belief, emotion and thought. In other words, our physiological self is a physicalized focus of our total consciousness. Please note that it is only one focus, one point of view, in our total fundamental consciousness, or what is commonly called the higher consciousness.

So you ask, "What about the rest of my consciousness? Where is it?" Well, I'm just as curious as you to find out. Remember that the main distinction of physical reality existence is the forgetting game. So having forgotten the rest of what we are, I consider it more useful to plunge into this reality, explore and enjoy it fully. Why? Because our consciousness obviously knows exactly what it's doing when it chooses this avenue of expression.

It is important to remember the knowledge that makes all the difference in how we experience this life in this reality. Our consciousness is *not* inside our bodies. Our bodies *exist within* our consciousness. This is power. This turns the game one hundred percent in our favor because this breaks down the door, the forgetting barrier, and allows us access to more and more of the power we are.

Why is this important? The answer lies in the nature of the forgetting game. With the total forgetting of all that it is that we are, we become limited to our physical world and physical reality. We get into the habit of thinking and acting in terms of the external physical world. We externalize *everything*. We get into the mode of thinking, feeling and believing that the real power is outside of ourselves. We get into the habit of believing that "things" happen to us because these "things" are not connected to ourselves. By shutting off our awareness of the fact that physiological beingness is only one way our consciousness expresses itself, we create the inability to see our connection to everything. Most importantly, this results in our inability to recognize that we *choose* the events in our lives.

As long as we remain creatures or beings who forget what we are, we lapse into externalizing everything. Therefore, we do not really recognize our responsibility for creating our physiological lives, nor do we take the initiative in creating it the way we prefer it to be. Since everything is seen as outside of the self, we struggle and fight to control things in order to feel powerful and in control of our lives. In other words, we lapse into negativity as we lose our inborn integral power—our integrity.

Again, because of the forgetting game, we do not perceive change as a simple matter of making conscious choices. I have said, in order to truly forget, we have to create means and places to hide things we do not wish to remember. Again, those are what we know as the subconscious and unconscious mind. So, sometimes, in order to change things, we may have to dig them out of these hiding places. Most of the time we store our beliefs and emotions outside of the conscious mind or out of conscious awareness.

How do we go about changing something we are not aware of? You will see. First, we must thoroughly understand the three-tiered model of thought, emotion, and belief. We will then proceed to explore how this serves us.

26

3

The Personality
Complex - Belief

B elief is our blueprint of physical reality. It is our general view
or notion about how the world is and about our ability to
function in it.

My young daughter once slipped and fell down on a sidewalk.
She sustained a large bump on the forehead and I knew that in the
next few days, the entire side of her forehead would become black
and blue. After she stopped crying from the initial shock and pain,
I assured her that by morning her forehead would be completely
healed because little girls heal very fast. I applied a cold compress
to the area and she went to sleep.

The next morning I was startled to find that not only was the
lump gone but that there was no discoloration or any residual
evidence of the injury whatsoever on her forehead. The child had
simply believed without a shadow of a doubt that she would heal in
a very short time. She believed and trusted my words. I, on the other
hand, coming from a different belief system (general medical
profession) was dumbfounded to see the effect of this child's simple
belief.

What happened here? How is this accelerated healing process
possible on a physiological level? The answer is simple. The brain,
the electrochemical apparatus which controls the body, is wired and
rewired according to our beliefs. In the case of this child, the brain
directed an accelerated healing process to the involved tissue.

Does belief apply to circumstances and events in one's life also? Absolutely. Events and circumstances in any one's life are nothing more than physical manifestations of our consciousness. All you have to do is examine an event in your own life. I'll share with you a significant event in my own life.

As a child growing up in a small African village, we used to gather around the local infirmary to watch the doctor arrive once a month to see the sick. My father and his attendants bustled around the infirmary presenting their toughest medical cases to the doctor. The doctor would ask a few questions, examine the patient and with seeming ease he would instruct them on what to do.

I was fascinated and decided that I wanted to become a doctor. My father smiled and nodded his approval. What my father didn't tell me then was that he knew that it would be impossible for me to study to become a physician given the reality of the time; rural Africa in the 1950s.

At the time, there were only two high schools for girls in the country, and science courses weren't taught in them. Nevertheless, he encouraged me to compete and secure admission to one of the schools. He was ecstatic when I succeeded even though he had no idea how he was going to pay my school fees. His meager salary could barely support the family. He had no hope of getting his friends and other members of his family to help financially because it was regarded as the height of folly to waste money educating a daughter .

Nevertheless, I became the first girl from my village to get a secondary school education. In high school I gathered information from the missionaries about what I had to do to get a medical education. I read about Madame Curie and about science and that inspired me. Botany and mathematics were the only science related courses taught. I kept my dream of becoming a doctor alive. In fact, I actually escalated it. You see, one of my instructors told me that the United States of America had the best medical education in the world. I didn't know where the United States was or much else about the country but I decided that that was where I would study to become a doctor. Again, my father would not discourage me. He took the greatest delight in my progress .

By the time I was a senior in high school, biology was introduced in my school. I remember excitedly memorizing whole lectures. I literally ate up everything we were taught. One month before graduation, the principal informed me that one of the boys' high schools in another part of the country would be offering coeducational courses in science. She offered to help me secure admission to that school.

Within one year I was in the United States as a premedical student in one of the finest colleges. I not only believed I could get into medical school, even when my I.Q. tests scores indicated that I couldn't make it through grade school, I believed that I would get into medical school in three years instead of the usual four. I planned and proceeded accordingly.

I became a United States physician against the greatest odds that the circumstances of my birth and environment could impose, not to mention being a foreigner, a woman and a black person, and with no money to boot. I have related this experience as an example of belief in action. Some of my friends just smile and say, "Vida, you have been a lucky woman!"

Luck is nice, but luck had nothing to do with it. Not really, especially if we look at it from the usual definition of luck, which is a gift which comes from outside of oneself.

Stripped of the charisma of "luck," here is what actually happened. I had a belief that I would become a doctor, and so I defined myself in this new light. Each belief carries with it all the attributes and built-in set of circumstances that will enforce the reality defined by that belief, as well as the capacity to bring it to pass.

Once my belief system defined me as a U.S. educated physician, the events necessary to bring this to reality, that is, into physical existence, seemingly lined up one after the other. Insurmountable obstacles that everyone else could see did not stand in my way. My belief content did not include or recognize insurmountable obstacles. Please notice that I did not say that it was easy. Things weren't easy, but the difficulties did not stop my persistence. In fact, they actually increased my excitement and realization of the worthwhileness of my goal.

For many years I have been curious about the nature of this explanation. It becomes clear only when we seek the explanation in the most basic terms, that is, in energy terms. After all, we are basically energy, just as everything else in existence is energy.

What distinguishes energy levels is their vibratory frequency. What distinguishes us as individual beings is the vibratory frequency of the energy unit at which we operate. Energy vibrational frequency is also what defines every object, every idea and event in existence. It is analogous to frequencies in a radio or television station. You can receive only the frequency you are tuned into. If the metaphysical channel you are tuned into is "Happy Days,"you are happy; however if your T.V. is on the "Twilight Zone", your emotional level is somewhere else. Identical or similar frequencies vibrate together. We may say that like frequencies attract each other, or belong together. In other words, one cannot experience an energy frequency that one is not the vibration of.

When my beliefs redefined my reality from a small village girl to a U.S. educated physician, my vibratory frequency got redefined into the vibratory frequency identification of a U.S. trained physician. That frequency can only operate or vibrate along the lines of people, events and circumstances that vibrate similarly or support that vibration. That explains why obstacles which could have, by every reasonable tenet, not allowed the reality to materialize, had no power to stop it. These probable or even highly likely obstacles did not operate on the same vibratory frequency of a reality blueprint of the unshakable belief system of a determined young girl. Having defined what my reality was to be by my belief, that definition attracted all that was necessary to see that reality manifest itself physically.

Beliefs are choices one makes and they are a system of those things one holds to be true. The choice can be conscious, subcon-

30

scious or unconscious. Thus, one may not be aware of a belief system which is the cause of an undesirable set of circumstances in life. As long as the belief system remains intact, the same desirable or undesirable events will continue to repeat themselves.

How does one find out what his belief systems are if they are buried in the deep dark recesses of the unconscious mind? Well, since beliefs are the blueprint of our daily experiences, they are the cause of the manifestations of that reality.

One way of uncovering a belief system is by observing its effects. For example, one brilliant businessman worked hard for many years to reach the top of his corporation, just before he was appointed president of his corporation, for no apparent reason, his behavior underwent a dramatic change. He began drinking heavily, got arrested for drunken driving, and eventually lost his job .

In going through his history, we discovered that he had exhibited the same pattern of near success and failure in his two previous occupations and even in his two failed marriages. It was as if this man was willfully sabotaging himself. He kept asking "Why is this happening to me?" He told us that he sincerely wanted to succeed and, in examining his past efforts, we could see that this was so. He was outraged when I suggested that perhaps he believed that he was unworthy of success .

"Then why would I work so hard to succeed?" He snapped.

"Because you may not know that you have that belief," I suggested.

He paced the floor thinking, "Now why would I feel that way?" he mumbled, frowning.

"Okay then," I said, "could you admit that you believe that way?"

"But," he began, raising his hands in protest.

"Would you rather argue, or would you prefer just to fix this thing?" I asked him. I took him through a belief change and future pacing to assure that he would behave in ways that are compatible with self-love and total deservedness. After he rescued his last business and turned it into a great success, he made a gratitude call

31

to me. He told me that he had developed a healthy respect for the power of beliefs. He said he watched the results of his actions. He regarded them as nothing but shadows of his beliefs. I suggested that he could install really powerful positive beliefs and create miracles in his life. "By the way, Doctor, how did I pick up these rotten beliefs in the first place?" he asked me later on. "In the same way as most of us do," I told him.

As children, we believe our parents because we trust them implicitly. We learn to survive and to live in the world by mimicking what they do. We literally absorb their beliefs and values. They form the basis of the reality we share with them and become the foundation of our lives. Most of these beliefs become an unconscious affair and we continue to run our world based on them, even when they don't serve any useful purpose to us any longer. They may in fact, serve a harmful or negative purpose.

In a similar manner, we acquire the belief systems of the culture or society in which we live. These beliefs may be negative or positive. To regard a system of beliefs as good or bad is a matter of pure judgement which is usually biased and so serves very little useful purpose. It is more practical to look on belief systems as desirable and serving a useful purpose for us, or undesirable and hindering us. In other words, beliefs can be regarded as positive or negative. Positive beliefs cause or create positive events and negative beliefs cause or create negative events. Which one is better? It depends on the individual's choice.

It is a general observation that the negative beliefs carry with them hardships, disease and unhappiness; positive beliefs bring with them the ease of creation, joy, and health.

As adults, we make conscious choices about what we believe and proceed to live with the results of those beliefs. Often the results are not what we intended them to be. Then we get baffled and say something like. "Why me? Why is this happening to me? I am a good person. I deserve better."

And you are right. Things would have turned out the way you would have preferred if you *knew* enough to make the proper choice

32

of belief to start with. However, nothing in life is cast in stone because change is a constant thing in existence. Because of this one fact, if we can (and we can) change our belief, then we can change the results to ones that we prefer.

The whole process of belief and its manifestation in reality can be compared to building a house. The belief is the blueprint and the resulting reality is the house. If the house, as it is being built, turns out to be something different than you had intended, you would generally go back to the blueprint and see where the errors had been made. You would then have them corrected or adjusted in such a way that you could proceed and build the house you desired. If you decided that the blueprint did not represent the house you wanted at all, you would simply replace it with another, more suitable, blueprint.

In actual practice, how is this done? First, you take a good look at the event you want to change from an unbiased and balanced viewpoint. This is most important. In other words, you accept that this particular event is your doing. That means that you don't deny that it is yours because you can't change what you don't own. Just as you can't change the color of your neighbor's car (not legally anyway) but can easily change your own, so you can't change an event that you don't believe that you created.

It is important to develop a resourceful attitude toward the undesired event by not condemning it. This becomes easier to accomplish once we bear in mind that the event is actually doing us a service; that, at the very least, it is occurring to let us see that it is not what we prefer. This circumvents the denial which does not allow us to make changes. Therefore, in the more resourceful, relaxed state of owning the events or owning up to the events as our doing, we find that it is easier to become aware of the beliefs which we are holding, and which are resulting in the current undesired events.

Once identified, these beliefs can then be changed. "But how?" most people would ask bewildered, while others would protest that it would take a lifetime to get over something they were born believing. Not so. Beliefs can be changed rapidly. It can be done as a conscious choice. For individuals who prefer rituals and the use of tools, neurolinguistic change work is very effective in changing beliefs.

A major task of metamedicine lies in the identification and change of belief systems held by the patient which stand in the way of healing and joyous good health.

Some of my surgeon colleagues and friends will no longer operate on patients who state that they will never get out of the hospital alive. They do this for a reason. Over the years, these competent surgeons have discovered that patients who believe that they will die, usually do. No surgeon worth his salt wants poor results, let alone a postoperative death. They have developed a healthy respect for a patient's belief about the results of his/her surgery.

A physician who is skilled in metamedicine can, by taking a good history, identify how and when the patient acquired the belief. Sometimes the belief is acquired through simple misunderstanding, as in the case of a young woman who believed that she would never survive an acute gallbladder operation. As she was waking up in the morning of her scheduled surgery, she overheard two rambunctious male interns discussing their sexual adventures. "What's your score at the O.R., Nick?" one intern yelled at the other.

"Nil," the second intern yelled back as he entered the young woman's room.

After that, this intern was baffled when the young woman refused to proceed with her surgery saying that she just knew that she would die. She had heard "O.R." (operating room) and "Nil," and made a picture of herself not surviving the surgery. She then incorporated it into her belief system. Beliefs can be acquired very fast because the human brain learns very fast. Once the source of her belief was uncovered, she proceeded with the surgery and made an uneventful recovery.

Sometimes it is not possible to uncover the source of the belief as in the case of superstitions. Then again, people quite often make generalizations about how things are and accept them as true. This is often the case in patients who believe that they will die from a disease because their parent and grandparents died of that particular disease. These, and other deeply held beliefs, can be changed quickly using neurolinguistic techniques, including time-line therapy. In making changes in belief systems, we generally replace an undesired belief with a more desirable belief system. We have found that we neither create energy nor destroy energy but merely change it. So it is with beliefs because beliefs generate with them the energy it requires to manifest them into physical reality. Since we are beings of total choice, we can choose and create the belief systems that will give us the life we desire. It is very exciting to recognize that we can create ourselves and our lives to be exactly what we want them to be.

4
Emotion

*"The final cause, then, produces motion
through being loved."*

Aristotle

In the hierarchy of the personality construct triad, emotion comes after belief and it precedes thought or mentality. Emotion means literally energy in motion, or more simply, energy motion. It is experienced physiologically as an internal feeling.

Emotion is a reaction to a belief. Let us watch emotion in action. For a moment imagine that you need a certain amount of money for something you desperately want. You do everything you can to obtain the money, to no avail. Then suddenly, you get a call from a friend who tells you that you have just won millions of dollars in the sweepstakes. You are surprised but you believe your friend. You react with a burst of joy and gratitude.

Had you not believed it, the news would not kick your feelings into such a high positive energy state. In fact, you may respond with mild annoyance and a slight depression if you believed that your friend was playing an unfair trick on you.

In the first instance, a positive belief was met by a positive emotion and in the second instance, a negative belief was accompanied by a negative emotion, the trigger being the underlying belief.

Why is emotion necessary? Let's go back to the analogy of belief as the blueprint of a house one desires to build.

It will take a certain amount of energy to construct this house out of the blueprint. The builders bring their energy, both mental and physical, to erect the house to the specifications of the blueprint. Emotion is analogous to the builders. It is the energy motion that brings the blueprint to reality. If you allow yourself to think about this, you will begin to appreciate the enormous power of emotion in determining what our lives become in the world.

Emotion, then, is the vibratory energy that allows us to create or bring into physical existence, that is physical reality, that which we want or desire. Again, as all energy is defined in terms of its vibratory frequency or wavelength, emotional energy is defined or described by its frequency.

As I have said, emotion, energy motion, is experienced physiologically as an internal feeling. These feelings range from the extremes of joy and laughter to fear and hate. In simple terms, these feelings run from polar opposites of the positive to the negative. In colloquial language, we describe these polarities of feelings as moods. We say , "I am in a good mood" or "I am in a bad mood." Given that good and bad are value judgements we place on these feelings, it is generally accepted that "good mood" means a positive, more desirable state of emotion, and "bad mood" means a negative, less desirable state of emotion.

One of my patients, Helen, told me once that she has her "down days" and her "up days." I persuaded her to explain to me what she meant by an "up day."

She looked uninterested saying, "Well, I really can't tell you now."

"Why not?" I asked her.

"Because right now I am having a down day," she explained.

"Alright, then tell me what a down day is," I suggested.

She looked uncomfortable and fixed her eyes to the floor.

"You can tell me," I urged her. "Just think about it for a moment."

She fidgeted on her chair for a moment and protested, "I can't explain it to you, Doctor."

Then it dawned on me that I was not asking her the proper question. By force of habit, training, and practice as a physician, I was relying on the powers of thought and rationalization to "figure things out." I remembered that an emotion is not what you think. It is what you *feel*. So I reversed course and addressed her feelings. "What if I offered to take this 'down day' for you, could you give yourself a vacation now?" I proposed, appealing to her sense of fun. "Show me how I could go about getting into a 'down day.' Begin with what would happen when I first wake up in the morning."

She smiled, rolled her eyes up to the left, cast a look down and said, "Well, you would open your eyes and look out the window. Then this dark film would fall down over your face." She pulled her right fingers down in front of her face.

"Oh, you mean, something would sort of shut off and darken the the sunlight," I interjected.

"Yes," she confirmed.

"What would I hear as I wake up?" I asked.

"Well, you would still hear the birds sing on the tree outside my window but, ..." she hesitated frowning.

"Yes, go ahead," I encouraged her.

"But it is not the same," she said.

"How is it different?" I asked.

"Their songs are not real happy. They are kind of slower and sadder," she explained.

"Okay," I said continuing, "what would I eat as a favorite breakfast?"

"Bacon and eggs," she answered. "But you wouldn't want to touch it."

"Why?" I asked curiously .

"Because you wouldn't be able to stand the smell of the bacon; it would make you want to throw up," she told me.

"Besides, you won't want to eat anyway because you won't be hungry," she added.

"Oh, I see," I agreed nodding convincingly. "Now, how would things feel when I touched them?"

"Everything will feel kind of cold all day," she answered. She spread her fingers, looked at them and wiggled them. "Your hands will feel kind of numb. Well, not exactly—it will feel as if you had plastic gloves on." After this she became silent and withdrawn.

I ventured one last question. "What will I be thinking of most of the day?"

She sighed and said, "You will think of all the things that aren't working out in your life—mostly your troubles."

"Thanks, you are an excellent teacher," I said with the conviction of one who has acquired the skills it takes to master misery. "Now you can begin to enjoy an 'up day'," I told her.
She gave me a puzzled look.

"Okay, here's what you do," I instructed her. "Close your eyes and imagine you are just about to get out of bed this morning." After she began to relax, I continued, "Now lift the curtain off your face as you open your eyes. See the bright morning sunlight streaming into the bedroom. Then hear the birds happily chirping away in the tree outside. Take a deep breath and fill your nostrils with the aroma of the delicious bacon your mother is cooking in the kitchen. All of a sudden you know you are hungry and you hurry out of bed to get ready for breakfast. You are thinking of all the terrific things to do today, your favorite activities you want to do today, such as ..."

"Like, go shopping," she volunteered opening her eyes, smiling and brightening up. It wasn't until she was on her way out of my office, that she realized fully that she was now in an 'up day'. She turned abruptly at the door and asked me with as much curiosity as concern, "Doctor, are you now having a 'down day'?"

"No," I answered her laughing. "I could have a 'down day' now if I choose to, but I choose not to."

Helen had described a negative emotional state. In teaching me how to get into this state, we learn what the positive state would be by contrast.

Listening to Helen describe a down day, I got the feeling that she was a battery, all I had to do was plug her into an electrical outlet to get her charged up. All her signals were flashing, "Low energy! Low vibration!"

How does one get into a state of high or positive energy motion (emotion)? How does one charge up? One of the ways is the same way Helen charged up that day—by changing the sensory modalities involved in the state. This is essentially how these changes are made in neurolinguistic programming, or NLP. Another way it is done using NLP is by anchoring the opposite emotional state and collapsing the undesirable emotions. This technique will be discussed in another section of this book.

In metamedicine, a much more powerful way to change emotions is to change the beliefs that triggered or generated the emotion to begin with. Recall that an emotion is a reaction to a belief. Change the belief and the emotion will change.

A young, single mother of a 6-year-old boy had struggled for years to get an education and acquire skills she needed to secure a job in order to get off welfare. About the time she landed a job as a computer operator she discovered that she was pregnant. Having another child would force her to stay on welfare and continue to raise her son in a very unhealthy environment. She made a decision to have an abortion.

During her immediate pre-operative period the nurses found her in severe depression and distress. She was crying uncontrollably. Her gynecologist advised her that she could change her mind about the surgery and keep the baby. That suggestion appeared to heighten her distress. She clearly needed help and I was asked to see her.

After establishing rapport with her, it was obvious from her history that her religious beliefs conflicted with her decision to terminate the pregnancy. She was suffering from a case of severe guilt which is a very unresourceful emotion .

"Do you know that the child you are carrying is another individual in its own right?" I asked her. She looked at me through her tears and nodded.

41

"Then we can say that in order for you to a have a baby, it would be necessary for you and the unborn child to agree to become mother and child?" I suggested. Again she nodded an affirmative.

"Do you fully sense that this unborn individual must have a great deal of love and respect for you just as much as you love and respect it?"

"Yes," she answered sobbing.

"Because of this love do you believe that this individual who is to be born is communicating with you and you are communicating with it at some level in your consciousness?" I asked. She gave me a puzzled look.

"Well?" I asked pressing for a response.

"I can't figure it out, but I feel it is like that," she allowed, curiosity lighting up her red eyes.

"The equal love allows you to match the unborn being's desires with your desires," I stated, watching her closely. "And, if at any stage, this individual, this being, decides not to go all the way and be born into this world, your feelings and decisions would match and you would agree that it shouldn't be born. And if it had decided to be born, you most likely would never have thought about abortion in the first place."

"I don't understand," she whispered. "Why wouldn't it decide to be born?"

"It may decide to have a body for just a little while—to see what being physical is like," I suggested as a probable explanation. "Well, it may just want to put a foot in to test the water, so to speak. It may not have wanted to buy the whole elephant—see what I mean? In either case, you did provide it with a loving service."

A faint smile spread across her lips, and I noticed a shift when she took a deep breath. "Thank you so much, Doctor," she said. "Now I understand."

When I came back in between surgical cases to check on her, I found her sleeping peacefully on the couch. She had acquired a positive new belief which replaced an old belief that viewed abortion as destruction of life. Accordingly, her emotion changed from despair to a positive energy state of peace.

Please notice that I made no attempt to impose my own beliefs and notice also that it was she who made the change. I only provided her with an alternative belief that she could and in this case did substitute for the old belief. There is no implication of right or wrong action in this incident. Right and wrong are judgements and in metamedicine we are only concerned with what is valid. Judgement is at best a denial of parts of our experience as being valid portions of our totality. As such, it denies us our full self empowerment. Take note that in order to judge, you would have to become the vibrational frequency of your judgement. Remember that you cannot perceive the idea unless you are the same frequency—the same wave length as that idea. Thus when as often happens, we judge an action to be negative, we are actually lowering our vibrational frequency to the level of this negative idea. So if one is to judge, it is more resourceful to judge a thing as positive or as providing a positive service. In order to do this all the time we really have to watch our judgements. As you can see, judging can become a pain in the posterior. Who needs it? It is much better not to judge at all. However, since we are all in the habit of making judgements, we should at least select positive ones.

"Are you saying that I can't accomplish what I set out to do even though my emotion is mostly negative?" one of my colleagues asked me once. My answer to that was, yes, he could. I explained that the route of negative emotion may not be the most enjoyable way of arriving at one's destination. By analogy, it would be the difference between flying first class from California to Hawaii, or travelling the same distance by paddling a canoe. The first method will get you there faster and in great comfort. The second may get you there barely alive, that is if you survive the weather, sharks and other hungry creatures.

Positive emotions such as joy, laughter and love add positive energy to a task and make it easier to accomplish. Many people, usually adults, would generally regard this statement as childish. "You are just being a Pollyanna," they say. "Life is hard, and there isn't much to be joyful about all the time." Those may be valid statements. The solution is a paradox. In order to have something to be joyful about all the time, one must first be joyful all the time. Here is why. Emotion creates a climate in which one functions or acts to bring anything into physical reality. With positive emotion, one is charged with positive energy enabling one to accomplish more positive things with ease. On the other hand, with negative emotion one is working in an atmosphere drained of energy—in a low energy state. It then requires application of tremendous effort to get anything accomplished.

Think for a moment about your school days. And if you are reading this book, it is a safe bet that you had some kind of formal education. Think of the classes or the courses you excelled in. What were your predominant feelings in these classes? Be honest with yourself. I'll tell you about mine. In fact, I will tell you about how I excelled in mathematics—a subject which didn't excite me and which to this day I tend to avoid.

I was lazy at mathematics, and I don't recall ever looking at a math problem out of sheer curiosity. I would only solve a math problem if I had to. This was unfortunate because I knew that if I was going to have a fighting chance at a medical education, I must demonstrate that I was good at mathematics.

First, I believed that I could excel in math if I wanted to. "Wanted to." Therein lay the rub. I was dragging myself through math getting mediocre scores when I began to entertain the foolish notion that the math instructor had a special interest in me. I developed a full blown crush for this instructor. Thereafter, my math scores soared. This of course, got my instructor's full attention, and the fireworks catapulted me to the top of the class!

By the way, here is what accelerated learning is all about. It is the creation of the proper emotional climate for optimum learning. Please notice that I did not say "optimum education." I am avoiding the word education because it generally implies some kind of schooling. Schooling in our current culture is a system for transforming learning into a difficult, uphill struggle. I am not invalidating it because it has served us. However, with the greater knowledge of what we are as human beings and how we function best, it is time to move on to better methods of learning.

In my small community, a few children who are considered to be specially gifted are selected from the various grade schools each year to attend special classes once a week. This program is called GATE. My 8-year-old daughter is in this program. My daughter has an intense dislike for school. Most mornings it is a battle to get her to agree to go to school, except on the day she goes to GATE. On GATE days, she gets up bright and early and urges me to get her to school an hour early. On GATE days she comes alive.

She teaches her father and I oceanography and astronomy—subjects she learned at GATE. I found them to be much more difficult subjects than her usual third grade courses. So I surmised that GATE was not all fun and games.

And I was wrong! It was. At GATE, learning *was* fun and games and the children gobbled it up at great speed. First, these children were taught to believe that they were very intelligent. They were treated as special by loving teachers who, by showing great interest in these children, reinforced their belief in their superior intelligence. Then the whole classroom atmosphere is charged with curiosity and excitement. The children learned difficult subjects with great ease.

I no longer battle with my daughter about school. All schools should be GATE because all children are gifted. Their gift is the privilege of being born into physical existence. All schools can provide the same emotional climate of positive energy provided at GATE in order to allow the children to learn easily and in an accelerated way.

The function of emotion in learning holds true for health. In fact, metamedicine views all disease or ill health as learning tools. This is why metamedicine expects a patient not only to survive an illness but to improve themselves by having gone through the disease progress. We always choose a disease to learn something—even if it is only to learn that we don't care for the pain of the disease.

This idea will be explored more in other sections of this book.

Many ancient and modern cultures in the world recognized the crucial role which emotional climate plays in health. As a child growing up in West Africa, I once lived among a tribe which was almost completely protected from all the advances of the twentieth century. Their sparkling rivers teemed with fish, and the forests were abundant with fruit, vegetables, and game. They had long ago achieved a balance with nature by respecting and nurturing it. So they were rewarded with abundance. This society enjoyed children and used their joy and laughter to provide healthy benefits.

The only purpose of marriage in that culture was to have children. To assure the health and fertility of a prospective bride, every effort was made to keep the bride-to-be happy. She was placed in pleasant surroundings a few months before the wedding. All day long she would be surrounded by children who played with her and kept her amused. Evidence of her happiness—her positive emotional state—was her physical appearance. Even scrawny prospective brides gained weight, blossomed, and became beautiful before the wedding.

When the new bride did conceive and give birth to a baby, the same ritual was practiced to assure that she would produce adequate breast milk to nourish the infant. Again she was kept in a joyous emotional climate by playful children and she was encouraged to be completely at ease in the postpartum period. In addition to allowing free flow of breast milk for the infant, it was important that she remain at ease so as not to transmit any feelings of tension to the new baby. It was believed that such conditions as colick, excessive crying and fevers were caused by tension in the mother.

Quite often when an adult became ill, the curer (a native doctor) would prescribe that the patient spend time alone with a loved one in a forest, to regain peace and balance in order to be cured of his or her disease.

This culture, by instinct, knew the importance of a positive emotional climate in health and disease. In western civilization, I have noticed that healing practices outside the mainstream of modern medicine both religious and otherwise are, more often than not, conducted in an atmosphere charged with elation, rousing joyous music, clapping of hands, and cheering. All in all, it is a high energy affair and while cure rates are unpredictable, they do enjoy a measure of success.

In cultures where voodoo curses and other such hateful rituals are practiced, negative emotions are used to drive the victims into fear in order to make them ill and even cause them to die. Fear is the opposite polarity of belief, and it is just as powerful. People will manifest what they believe or what they fear. In other words, we say that fear is belief in the negative. A victim of fear is choosing negative belief. Having established the negative belief, the victim responds with negative emotions. These negative emotions are then fueled and fanned by the antics and ritual of the voodoo priests and all the fearful people who usually are attracted to these situations. In this negatively charged climate, the victim proceeds to manifest the curse in the form of an illness, accident or even death.

A victim is a creature who is so immersed in negativity that it believes all power to be outside of itself and all its situations to be imposed by these outside forces. This negativity causes the victim to create more separations between its totality and its limited physical self. With extreme fear, the negativity is of such magnitude that the victim is incapable of perceiving that it has a choice to accept or reject the conditions.

Modern medical science is increasingly becoming aware of the vital role that a patient's emotion plays in disease states. The high incidence of mortality and morbidity in heart disease has been responsible for forcing attention on the personality of patients in recent years.

People classified as having type "A" behavior traits are found to be impatient, driven workaholics who seek to control everything in their environment. These individual have been found to be prone to heart disease and related ailments.

There are also the class of people whose dominant traits are helplessness, hopelessness, and fear. Unlike the type A behavior patterns, the destructive behavioral pattern in this group has to do with denial of their own power. It has been found that most cancer patients fall into this group. This group is also the one that tends to suffer from immune-related diseases like rheumatoid arthritis and AIDS (Auto Immune Deficiency Syndrome). These diseases which have to do with loss of the body's natural barrier to infections, mirror the inner giving up of control and power by the patient.

These personality behavior traits both stem from the same fundamental flaw—lack of trust in one's own power. The type A emotional pattern demonstrates an attempt to gain control over others and the self in order to feel powerful. These individuals do not believe that they are powerful enough to get anything they want without hurting themselves or someone else. The helpless/hopeless/fearful personality traits are a denial of one's own power. This group of individuals refuse to acknowledge or take responsibility for their own power. They literally abandon themselves to despair and their bodies and immune systems mirror this abandonment.

A tense (negatively charged) emotional climate breeds diseases of tension such as hypertension and cardiac disease. Cancer and immune related diseases point to negative emotional climates wherein the victim has abandoned (denied) his or her own power.

All disease is just that—*dis*-ease (literally). A condition in which one is not at ease with all that one is. Diseases reflect accurately one's emotional or energy state and as such are fascinating reflections of what is going on at the deepest level of physiological existence.

Physicians who treat cancer patients have noticed the many interesting correlations between survival and the patient's attitude. Much has been reported in medical literature of the rare patient who recovers completely from a cancer that is known to always be fatal.

Dr. Bernie Siegel, who has done much work in investigating this phenomenon and who is the founder of Exceptional Cancer Patients, Inc., noted that it is not usually the nice, submissive, patients who survive cancer. He noted that those patients who get angry and refuse to yield have had better records of survival. In fact, he frequently urges cancer patients to get aggressive and take matters into their own hands, as opposed to leaving their fate in the hands of their doctors. Many doctors still do not like the aggressive patient and some doctors would consider these patients hostile and terminate relations with them.

This is unfortunate because an aggressive patient is, at the very least, recognizing that he or she does not have to accept their condition as a life sentence. Even though aggression is an unnecessary attitude, that is, if one truly trusts in ones own power, those patients that get angry show that they have doubts about their prognosis. Doubt is a step in the direction of change in belief. Quite often, those patients who refuse to passively accept their condition, do achieve belief change. They begin to believe that they can survive in spite of statistics which say otherwise. When they do get well, we call them exceptional patients and everyone else calls the event a miracle. The paradox is that these patients truly come close to having what should be regular normal behavior or traits and the so-called miracle is actually what should happen on a regular basis, that is, if they knew how to live.

If we knew what we are and how to live, we would appreciate the fact that achieving any healing at all in our current state of universal negativity is the true miracle. Look at it this way. We have a very competent surgeon who had just done a breast biopsy to confirm what he already knew—that Mrs. Humphrey, a pleasant submissive woman, has breast cancer. She knew that she had a lump in her left breast three years before she finally mentioned it to anybody.

"Oh," she said to the doctor during her first visit, "I have a small lump in there, but I don't think its anything really. I came because my daughter insisted that I come to see you."

"Mrs. Humphrey, you say you've had this for three years?" The doctor asked incredulous, "Didn't it ever occur to you that it may not be normal?"

Mrs. Humphrey didn't answer. She looked down to the floor and tears rolled down her plump cheeks.

Later in discussing with her and her husband the details of the surgical and therapeutic procedures that needed to be undertaken to help Mrs. Humphrey, the surgeon refrained from painting any positive pictures about the outcome of the therapies. It was not exactly his fault that he did so.

In the pursuit of objectivity as the proper scientific attitude in medical education, physicians are prone to emotional detachment in their approach to the patient and his/her illness. In recent years, medical practice in most parts of the United States has become a strange legal game. Some patients and their lawyers have come to look on major surgery as a lottery where a fortune can be won. The outrageous sums of money awarded by various juries in malpractice litigation around the country instigate and nurture this attitude. My husband has coined the name "litigo" for this game. It has forced physicians across the nation to address patients as if the patient's lawyer is in the examining room, listening to every word.

So the surgeon spoke with Mrs. Humphrey and her husband in a pervading atmosphere of distrust and veiled hostility. It wasn't until after the formal visit was over that the doctor took Mrs. Humphrey's hand and patted her shoulder to show some compassion and encouragement.

What do we have here? First, we have an individual who has cancer, and who does not believe in her own power. Anyone skilled in metamedicine could lead her to see that this was a great opportunity she was giving herself to discover her power as a living being. However, this did not happen and it was business as usual. She comes from a negative emotional frequency. Her surgeon, in proceeding with the prevalent negative attitude typical of this age, had intensified this negative climate. And both parties were hoping for a positive outcome! Now you can appreciate why I say that it will indeed be a miracle if Mrs. Humphrey achieves a cure.

The outcome of every act that we perform as human beings is largely dependent on the emotional climate in which it occurs. The emotional climate is what fuels the action with its energy, and it is that energy that determines whether a positive or a negative out-

50

come is achieved. This is why an underdog team in an athletic event quite often will soar to victory when the spectators go into a frenzy cheering them. Those who have ever been in a religious revival meeting can literally feel the energy of the moment in their bones as the spirit of the congregation explodes with praise and joy. At that moment, Scrooge himself may happily empty his pocket into the collection plate, then proceed to sign a pledge to turn over ten percent of his life savings to the organization. Emotion is one of the greatest tools for selling anything. Fear, a negative emotion, can drive an entire nation to war. Even without understanding a word of German, anyone watching films of Hilter's rallies can feel the power of a master manipulator of negative emotions. Generating positive emotions of love and faith has generated millions of dollars for evangelists all over the world. This breed of skilled emotional manipulators can induce perfectly rational individuals to turn over immense amounts of their cash to them.

I remember listening to Oral Roberts one morning when I was a very poor medical student living in a run-down apartment of a tenement building. I became so engulfed in emotion that I mailed him five dollars—my entire week's grocery money—without thinking about it. The strange thing was that he did not convince me of anything; he just roused my feelings, and that compelled me to make my maximum contribution! Twenty years later, after I studied neurolinguistic programming, I understood what actually happened.

I hear complaints all the time of "Doctor, I am anxious and depressed and I can't do anything about it." My patients are not unique in this observation. Most of humanity, including myself, quite often find ourselves plagued by uninvited emotions invading the routine of everyday life.

Depression is considered to be the worst emotion that plagues us. "Doctor, I feel down," my patients complain, "I just don't feel like doing anything."

When depression becomes incapacitating, most sufferers will seek medical help. They may see a psychiatrist or their family doctor. Usually a diagnosis of depression is made or confirmed and the patient more often than not, gets medications to help alleviate the problem. In other words, we treat the symptoms.

"So, what is wrong with that?" my colleagues would ask.

"Nothing," I would say. Then I explain that it would have been more fun and much more powerful if we took the metamedicine approach to the problem. We would then ask the question, "What is this emotion we call depression?"

Depression is going or turning inwards. It is the same as the act we call meditation except that it is judged as negative. Depression is meditation judged.

"And what do we turn inwards to do?" my patients ask.

We turn inwards for clarity or for balance. Once clarity is attained, a shift (balance) occurs, and we translate that as a feeling of peace. We have reached an emotional equilibrium.

This is essentially what happens in the practice called "Focusing." Recognizing that we operate on conscious, subconscious, and unconscious levels, we relax and ask ourselves what the feeling of depression is all about. We trust our feelings to sort things out. No judgement whatsoever is made on feelings that surface. Those feelings are merely observed and questioned until we notice a shift. Most people describe the shift as a feeling of a heavy load falling off their bodies, or simply as a feeling of peace. After that, they say that they feel all right. They get back their energy and are capable of resuming their normal activities.

If we didn't complicate a normal phenomenon of seeking balance inwards with judgement, it would not be necessary to go through drug therapies or any other therapies whatsoever. Watch how a child handles a down time or what grown-ups interpret as depression. The child exhibits sadness at first, then cries and that takes care of the matter. Is it that simple? Yes, it is.

Crying and laughter are emotions that center or balance us— when they are not judged. When crying is judged by the crying individual as a negative emotion, it becomes negative. Recall that I stated earlier that one becomes the vibration frequency of the energy one is judging. You have to lower your energy to the same wave length as the energy of your judgement. So when I judge my crying as a negative act—my energy level would have to match and become negative. Therefore, I have not achieved balance—the zero rest point of emotional energy.

"You can't expect me to cry. I am a man," I hear the male patients assert. "It is so embarrassing to cry," some of my female patients confide. This reflects the curse of adulthood, the deeply held notion of what one should be instead of what one naturally is. We can learn a lot about how to live life by watching children. In addition to giving adults a chance to know what love is again the main reason for having children is so we can, by watching them, relearn what we have forgotten—how to live fully in the eternal now.

Laughter, which most people are not embarrassed about, is another act or tool that can get us to the zero rest point of energy emotion—to the balance point.

Here is a maneuver or short therapy which Richard Bandler, the co-developer of NLP, devised. Think of a problem that overwhelms you. Now imagine telling that problem to an individual you extremely respect or admire, that is, someone who is your hero or idol. Now having told your troubles, watch your hero burst out laughing. He/she falls down laughing and can't seem to stop laughing. Now open your eyes and think about your problem again. Most people will discover that their feelings or emotions connected with the problem have now undergone a dramatic change. Most people will feel neutral about the problem that used to upset them so much. Others will actually begin to smile or laugh about it. A few individuals may get angry. This is quite a shift from being paralyzed by fear.

The bottom line is that once the emotional gear has been shifted into a more resourceful state, the individual is no longer a victim. He or she can proceed to solve the problem in a more resourceful emotional (energy) climate.

What is the importance of centering, or the centered state? I have shared the idea that the centered state is the zero rest point on the energy (emotion) continuum. The zero rest point is where we are identical to the energy out of which we are created. In other words, we identify with the frequency of the electromagnetic energy of our physiological origin. We become that wave length. In that state— that zero rest point—there can be no *dis*ease or stress. We momentarily recreate ourselves in perfection, so to speak. From the zero rest point, we can then choose the situations or outcomes that we wish.

It is important to understand the idea of the zero rest point. Quite often, when we make positive changes in ourselves and things are going well for us, we begin to wonder and worry about how long the new changes will last. "I wonder how long this will last before hard times hit again," we think. "Things are just too good to be true. This can't last." We live with the fear that "Murphy's Law" will get us. Understanding the "zero rest point" will put this kind of belief to rest.

When you are presented with a situation, that situation is essentially neutral. This means that it has no built-in meaning. We use our own judgement to interpret it as good or bad, as positive or negative, if you will. To illustrate, suppose you come upon the wreckage of an airplane. This is a neutral event. All you see is a bunch of airplane parts on the ground. You may say to yourself, "This is awful, think of all those poor people who must have been killed." You have supplied a negative meaning to this event and you feel bad.

Now suppose on the other hand, that you found out that the manufacturer had discovered the plane to be defective and had scrapped it in order to prevent an accident. You will think "What a safe and smart thing this is!" And you will feel good.

The situation or appearance of the thing hadn't changed a bit. All that changed was your feelings about it. In order to go from a negative feeling, "feeling bad," to a positive feeling, "feeling good," you had to stop and then make a conscious choice to do so.

You don't shift from the positive into the negative automatically. You always go to the zero rest point first. From there you make a conscious decision to move in another direction. Look at it this way: Let positive and negative choices be represented by two mountain peaks and the zero rest point be the valley between them, as illustrated below.

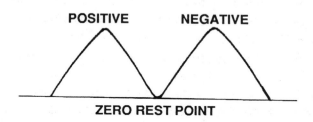

POSITIVE   **NEGATIVE**

ZERO REST POINT

You can climb whichever mountain you choose. If you fall off one of them, you don't automatically land on top of the other (unless you defy the law of gravity). You have to land at the zero rest point first. From there you can *choose* to climb the positive or the negative mountain before you actually do so. The zero rest point is always the point of balance from which you can choose whatever you wish in your reality.

Notice that when I describe Richard Bandler's "falling down laughing" therapy, I had you do the maneuver in your imagination. Imagination—that is the magic word which eludes description! When I tell people to use their imagination, most of them protest that they don't have any or that their imagination is poor. Not so.

Imagination is the medium of operation of all consciousness. Everyone has as much imagination as they need for whatever they want because everyone is a consciousness. In other words, if you are conscious, you are accessing your imagination all the time. Everytime you think, you use imagination. This will be explored further in the next section on mentality (thought). Everything you do, you first create in your imagination, then you proceed to act it out. You do this so quickly and so automatically that you don't realize you've done it. This is why people think that imagining requires a special ability. The only thing that requires this so-called special ability is belief, or trust that one is indeed continuously using the imagination.

NLP is a new technology that renders a large part of modern psychiatry obsolete. Using this technology, or tool, rapid changes are made in the personality make-up of an individual. Changes can be made in the belief system, the emotions and the thoughts to achieve a desired outcome, and this can be done without lengthy therapy sessions that go on for years.

We process the information from the world around us (our reality) by using our five senses. NLP makes use of the observation of how the mind processes the information from these senses for making changes internally and externally—that is, behaviorally. The five senses or sensory input channels are:

> *Visual (vision)—the channel which includes what we
> see with the eyes and the way everyone sees us.
> *Auditory—what we hear with our ears and the way it
> sounds, words and the way people say the words to us.
> *Kinesthetic—external feelings including touch,
> pressure and the texture of things.
> *Olfactory—the sense of smell.
> *Gustatory—the sense of taste.

There are at least two additional sensory channels available to human beings, but their discussion is not within the scope of this work.

Using the NLP model, rapid changes in emotional states can be accomplished by manipulating the internal representation of information received from the sensory channels. The most exciting breakthrough which NLP provides is that permanent changes can be made, often without cognition of the underlying causes.

This supports the Metamedicine concept that cause and effect are the same or that the cause reflects the effect. Using the methodology of NLP then, a person troubled by an unwanted emotion can be returned to a neutral state (the zero rest point), and then can be guided to a more resourceful state of emotion. This is of utmost importance in achieving optimum health in every way and in becoming that which one wants to be in this life.

Emotion is energy motion and it is the frequency of this vibratory energy that determines what we do and the degree of our excellency in doing what it is that we do.

"How do I know that I am doing what is right for me?" my patients frequently ask. The answer to this question is what I consider to be the greatest tool for living that we have available at any given moment in life—excitement or desire.

Excitement is the emotion which lets us know that we are on the right track to being what is true for us. It's what lets us know that what we are excited about is indeed right for us. Excitation is used in physics to raise the energy level of atoms, electrons, etc. It is the basis for generating the energies of lasers and reactors. The same principle of excitation applies to human activity because we are energy also. Excitement or desire is the vibratory frequency of one's core vibration—which defines the purpose(s) of one's life in this world.

"But I don't know the purpose of my life," many people protest.

"Just follow your excitement," I urge them. Excitement is the energy beacon that will lead you to it.

"Well, I don't get excited about much," a lot of discouraged people confess.

"What do you expect—an earthquake maybe?" I sometimes ask them. I explain that excitement doesn't mean that they feel like jumping up and down all the time. Any time you are doing what really interests you or what you desire to do, you are doing what exites you.

Please note that excitement describes momentum, as opposed to titillation. Excitement is the momentum that infuses ordinary tasks with positive energy. It can be an indicator of an action which is in line with our core vibratory frequency or it can be the motivational energy for a task which holds little appeal for us.

As an example, given a choice of two jobs, one job may

definitely appeal to us and grab our interest. If we act on this impulse, we will find that it is a job we will enjoy and at which we will be successful. On the other hand, when we must do an unattractive job, such as filling out the income tax returns, we can search our brains for any pleasant circumstances in relation to such a chore. I find that the most exciting thing about filling out the return is finishing that job and having it behind me. Therefore, I would invoke a feeling of looking forward to completing this task and the momentum of this positive feeling would motivate me to actually do the job quickly.

Why is it important to generate excitement and momentum in doing a job that does not appeal to us? It is because flowing with excitement creates ease and avoids stress. Forcing ourselves to do that which holds a negative interest to us is like going against the grain. One gets splinters that way. Excitement and momentum prevent friction. Friction is the source of pain and stress.

We circumvent friction and stress by keying into those things that attract our interest or excitation at any given moment. The momentum for that positive energy can then carry us through all the other tasks that we perform at that time.

It is acting on the opportunities which attract our interest at any given moment that allows us to discover who we truly are. When we are being truly ourselves, being focused and acting in a positive way becomes easy and natural. This is true for those jobs that we are truly excited about. When we are doing what we are about, we are essentially vibrating in tune with what we are meant to be. Therefore, we find the action to be effortless, enjoyable and really pure joy. How does the saying go? — "A labor of love is no labor at all." People who are doing the work that excites them the most will tell you in confidence that they don't know why anyone pays them for their work because they are enjoying themselves immensely. And it follows that the job that excites them the most is the job they excel in and, therefore, the occupation that earns them the most. If a business man could select and staff his office with people whose excitement lay in the direction of being file clerks, secretaries, etc., think of what a dynamite team he would have.

We have found that patients recover much faster from a disease when they follow their excitement.

"Come on now, Vida," my skeptical colleagues would respond to this statement. "How can a post-operative patient, confined to a hospital bed, get out and do what excites them the most?"

"As long as they are alive and conscious, they can take action," I insist.

You see, the human brain does not know the difference between an imagined act and what we consider a real act. If you imagine your favorite dessert, your mouth will salivate just as if you actually had that dessert sitting in front of you. In either case your brain gave the signals for your mouth to water in anticipation of eating the dessert.

A surgeon who encourages his patients to imagine eating their favorite foods can induce earlier return of intestinal motility, even after extensive bowel surgery. These patients can then begin eating earlier and be discharged from the hospital sooner.

After giving birth to a premature infant, I lost a lot of blood—almost half of my blood volume. I was very weak and ran high fevers to boot but I refused blood transfusions because it would force me to be confined to my hospital bed. And I wanted to be with my infant that day more than anything else I could think about. Even though I was almost too weak to walk, touching my tiny daughter (birth weight one pound, fourteen ounces) filled me with strength. I looked around the intensive care unit for premature babies and none of those tiny beings were clothed. Naked, those babies all looked like starved lizards. No wonder some frightened parents refused to visit them. I urged my husband to immediately go out and buy a dress for our daughter. He returned after a long time with a dress for a toy doll. He couldn't find clothes for premature babies anywhere in the city. He was told that no companies made or carried clothes for these tiny ones. I sent my husband back to the stores to buy me some yardage and sewing materials. That night in my hospital bed, I sewed a dress for our daughter.

After I put it on her, she looked just like a regular baby. Everyone began behaving differently around her—there was more acceptance. Right then, I had a desire to see all premature babies dressed in soft baby clothes. I got very excited about the idea and somehow found a way to make trips into stores to gather materials for the project. I used my daughter as a model for the clothes I designed.

The story of my venture got into the newspapers. Six weeks later, Broadway, a major retail department store chain, began selling a line of clothes for premature babies!

Such is the power of excitement. What did following my excitement really do for me? It induced a much faster recovery for me by energizing me physiologically. Medically, without blood transfusions, it would have taken many weeks for me to recover enough to get around. I was out of the hospital within days and nobody knows when my blood count (CBC) returned to normal. Who cares? As far as I was concerned, I was well again.

This is the basis of accelerated healing and all so-called miracle healings. Following one's excitement is what balances and aligns one within the natural electromagnetic energy field of one's physiological origin. In that state there can be no disease.

Please note that this does not invalidate the use of any medical regimen to alleviate a disease condition. All tools are valid— especially if the belief system of the patient incorporates them. As I said before, in the end, it is the body which actually heals itself. Medicines, surgery and any other tools are just that, tools. They merely provide suitable conditions wherein the body can heal.

Desire or excitement is the energy signal one can rely on to lead one in the path of health, happiness and wealth. With integrity, it generates and amplifies positive thought, which leads to right action in every phase of living.

The highest emotional energy level in existence is love, unconditional love. At this energy level all beings become the same energy. This energy is what makes telepathy possible because, being of identical energy, two individuals can directly become

60

alike. They can know and feel exactly what the other one is feeling and thinking. It can truly be said that love is the energy material out of which we are made. It is the primordial substance of beingness. It is quite often reported that two people who are deeply in love can know exactly what is on each other's mind.

Please note that I said unconditional love—love without judgement and with no questions about deserve-ability. By loving everything in life, one gets to see that every event, every experience and everything else in one's life has served or is serving a purpose. One gets to see that no event has a built-in meaning. All events and situations are neutral and only take on the meaning we give them. Unconditional love lets you feel that everything is equal and since it is a condition of the highest energy, you can't help but infuse all events with positive meaning. Thus you will let all events become of positive service to you.

"No thanks, Doctor Vida," one of my allergy patients once said to me. "There is no way I am going to love the fact that I am allergic to cats."

"What have you learned from your allergy disorder?" I asked her.

"What is there to learn?" she protested bewildered. "I hate my allergy. Why, I am almost a prisoner in my house. All my neighbors keep cats!"

"Oh, I see," I said, "then that's what you've learned."

"What do you mean?" she asked.

"You told me that you do not like the fact that you are allergic to cats," I reminded her. "That, at a minimum, is what you have learned."

I then proceeded to take her through the allergy cure, which is a fast reprogramming process. Briefly, the process consists of having the patients watch their dissociated selves interact by degrees with that which they are allergic to. Then they integrate themselves and go through the same maneuver.

She was amazed at the positive result. Weeks later, after she adopted a cat from the local animal shelter, she asked me to explain to her why that simple exercise worked.

"I don't know why it worked for you," I told her. "What does your imagination tell you about the reason it succeeded?"

She was silent for a while. Her eyes defocused, and she appeared lost in thought.

"Well, Doctor," she voiced finally, "I believe that I got a part of me to accept cats. I think that's what happened."

"Wonderful!" I cried with delight, "so how are you going to live from now on?" I asked her.

"I think maybe if I take the attitude of accepting things, I probably won't develop allergies anymore," she answered solemnly.

"Ah, unconditional acceptance," I added.

"I think so," she agreed.

Now, unconditional acceptance goes hand in hand with unconditional love. "Now Vida, you've gone too far with this," some people protest. "It would be insane for anyone to accept some of the horrible conditions we find in the world," they point out.

That is a valid statement. However, unconditional acceptance does not mean preference. Preference is essentially choice. One can choose to prefer or not prefer a thing or a condition. Unconditional acceptance means that one accepts without judgement that a thing or an event is valid and that it has a place in one's reality. Unconditional acceptance is, therefore, non-denial of anything, or any event, in one's life. It is simply accepting responsibility for one's reality. It is only by recognizing the validity of these events that allows the individual to choose if he/she prefers them or not.

Preference can be seen as choice. Unconditional love and acceptance are the bias-free media that permit us to make the most resourceful choice. Choice is freedom, which is one of the most treasured of human values. It is the birthright of all human beings.

Choices can be viewed as the signals we give ourselves to proceed to action. Positive choices lead to positive thought and positive outcome. Negative choices lead to negative thought and negative outcome.

A crucial task in metamedicine is the research into choices made by the sick. Once the unresourceful choices are recognized by the patients, they are encouraged to allow themselves to create other choices. They can then pick from among these the ones that they prefer.

Preference or choice, is the bridge connecting emotion to thought, and thought generates all physical action.

5
Thought
(Mentality)

"All that a man does outwardly is but the expression and completion of his inward thought."

-Channing

Thought is the third facet of the personality construct and it is the aspect most familiar to us. Thought is the part of the personality which mediates between the person and reality. Often referred to as the ego, thought is what focuses us to the physical world and what we use to interact with the world in order to build the type of life we live. It is thought that determines the quality of one's life.

Let us return to the analogy of a person (person's life) as a house. I have described belief as the blueprint of the house. Emotion is the energy—positive or negative, that triggers its construction. Thought can be viewed as the materials with which the house is built and the director of the physical act of construction. If we choose good (positive) materials, we will build a strong (positive) house. If we use weak (negative) materials, we can still build the house but it will be an unstable or flimsy (negative) house.

How does this work in day-to-day living? In general, we are usually vaguely aware that we want to do something or that we don't want to do it before we proceed with actually performing the action. Let's get specific. We get up in the morning and get out of bed because we know that we are going to go to our job. We are either aware that we have a desire to go to work or that we fear what might happen if we don't go to work. Nonetheless, we know that we are going to work.

Once we get to work, we have the option to do a good job, that is productive work, or to sleep on the job. What option we choose will depend on what created our desire to go to work, or fear to stay home, in the first place. Most likely we had envisioned ourself as affluent or we feared a vision of ourself as a pauper. We then matched our thinking and actions at the job against these visions. More often than not, this is done outside of conscious awareness. If we have an idea of ourself as the affluent version, we will proceed to take only actions that will lead to productivity. If our vision is fear of poverty, we may refrain from sleeping on the job and getting fired.

By now we can see that in day-to-day living, we use our belief as a reference index to determine if what we are thinking of doing is right for us or not. We can appreciate that it is also our belief that generates the feeling or emotion of desire or fear which causes us to think about taking action. All this drama goes on in the mind continuously.

The mind, physiologically functioning as the brain, directs all activity of the personality complex through thought. The level of the activity to be performed is dictated by the emotional energy (desire) of the idea, which in turn is dependent on the belief system generating the emotion.

The electrochemical organ known as the brain uses five major sensory pathways to interact with the world. These sensory pathways or channels are as follows:

* The visual channel: what we see and how we see it.
* The auditory channel: what we hear and the way it sounds to us, also, if it sounds right or makes sense to us.
* Kinesthetic: the sense of touch, how we feel the world and the way the world feels to us.
* Olfactory: the sense of smell.
* Gustatory: the sense of taste.

The brain's mental process receives information from the world around us, using these five senses. From this information, the brain develops for us a composite view of our reality. Thus, what we experience is a combination of what our eyes can see, what we hear, what we feel externally and internally and to a lesser extent, what we smell and taste. The way these are blended or integrated together is unique to each individual, so that each individual's reality or point of view of the world is unique. In a sense, each person's point of view is his or her personal signature written on the face of the world.

The brain can utilize all the sensory channels in actual or real time or on an imaginary basis. Using this we can perform an action now. As an example, see a red flower now. And we can also imagine an action now. Construct an image of the same flower in blue. In either instance we can store the images of the flower in our brain and remember or recall them at other times. The medium or screen on which we project these stored or formed images is what we call the Imagination. It is the internal medium or projection screen on which we create and manipulate images using thought patterns. Knowing how to use the thought processes of the mind to effect changes in our lives is the same as knowing how to use our brains to make changes in our personality makeup. The brain is an organ for learning. It constantly receives and evaluates input from our world and having processed it using thought patterns, it responds by generating a certain behavior. The quality of this process is highly influenced and dependent upon the emotional climate and belief system of the individual at the moment of the events. So how does the brain do what it does and how do we work with it to get what we want? Unfortunately, we are not born with an owner's manual for our brains. However, we are born with a lot of curiosity with which we can tap into the brain to learn how it works.

One of the greatest breakthroughs in this area in recent years is the discovery and development of Neurolinguistic Programming by Richard Bandler and John Grinder. NLP explains how the brain processes or codes information. It describes the process of communication of information between us and the world around us (including other people) in this way:

Using the five sensory channels, we (the brain) make an internal representation of this information and after that, the information is modified or shaped by one's beliefs, values, memories and something called meta-program. NLP calls these modifiers filters. The filters function by generally deleting, generalizing or distorting the original information received from the sensory channels to a degree. The filtered down thought patterns of the original information are what generate a physiological response or behavior, subject to one's internal (emotional) state at the time .

To illustrate, I once took my daughter, then two and a half years old, to one of her regular checkups at her pediatrician's office. She was tense and hung onto my hand. The nurse's smile, Disneyland figures on the wallpaper of the examining room and the offer to hold on to a Teddy bear did little to entice her to let go of me. She wanted to go home.

She was measured, examined and given her immunizations as usual. Later that day her father asked her if she had fun at the pediatrician's office.

"Na ha," she said, shaking her head. "The doctor hit me on my head and bit my bottom," she reported!

When I recovered a measure of composure from laughing, I explained gently that things didn't exactly happen that way at the pediatrician's, and that the pediatrician had measured her height and given her a shot. She glanced up to her left and her little face became very serious. "Na ha, Momma. She hit my head. She really did," she insisted with conviction.

Here we have filters at work. My daughter's past negative memory of "visits to the baby doctor" and her belief that nothing but pain can come from such a visit, had the effect of distorting the events in her internal representation of it. When she reported that the pediatrician had hit her on the head and then bit her bottom, that to her, was her actual experience. That was her point of view of the events.

On the other hand, what I saw was a pediatrician's office set up like a child's dream playhouse. The nurses clearly liked children. They beamed with delight, talked to them and played a little with them to put them at ease. All involved were very gentle with their tiny patients. My experience of the entire event was pleasurable. Obviously, my filters–my memories and values–have *distorted* and *generalized* this event, which I represented internally as a totally pleasant one. It possibly could not all have been pleasant. What about the part where my daughter flinched and cried out while getting the shot in her rear? Notice how I had *deleted* that part? It didn't fit into the little pleasant memory of the event I had recorded internally. I came to this event comparing the pleasant surroundings of the pediatrician's office with the stark, cold, threatening environment of the hospital operating room. In those days this was where I did my work as an anesthesiologist. Operating room work for the most part was a grim affair. The fearful patients were usually quite drugged before their arrival at the O.R., a far cry from the energetic curious kids romping on the floor of the pediatrician's waiting room. The seriousness of the O.R. atmosphere can be quite suffocating. Once in a while an unusual surgeon like my husband, would interrupt the tension by telling a ludicrous story or a joke. In more recent years, I have taken to playing classical music during surgery with remarkable effects.

It is plain to see how I would come to value the pediatrician's office and environment as an ideal place to work. This value judgement and my memory of hospital operating rooms, bent and colored my experience of my daughter's visit to the pediatrician that day.

So, who has the real picture of what transpired at the pediatrician's office? No one. No one has the total experience as it happened. Everybody involved has their own version of it. Even as I tell it now, you the reader, have your own imaginary views or versions of that event.

Is it important that we know exactly what really happened? No. The capacity to have as many versions of the event as there are people, adds richness to any experience. The idea that internal representation is not a precise description of the event is the concept in NLP known as "The map is not the territory." A map is just a representation of the territory it depicts, and one picks out those portions that help one get to the chosen destination in the territory.

The idea that we create our own version of all experiences of any event is real power and a crucial step in metamedicine. With this knowledge, it does not take much deduction before one can begin to perceive that most likely, no event has any built-in meaning or that we are the ones who supply the meaning by creating our own versions of the event. If you have ever attended a newsworthy event and incredulously asked yourself, "Was I really there?" after reading a reporter's version of it, you would know what I mean.

As long as we give an event its meaning, why don't we give it the meaning that would serve our purposes the best? Why not give it the meaning that would create the most joyous and powerful response? We can if we want to, by running our brains. If we don't, the brain will keep running anyway. As Richard Bandler said, the brain is a machine without an "off" switch. The danger in this is that if we are in the habit of living in fear, the idle brain can really scare the living daylights out of us by turning a neutral event into a nightmare.

How to run our own brains and control our thought processes is described by NLP methodologies. Full description of this fascinating subject is beyond the scope of this work. There are some excellent books available on the various elements of NLP. The quality of one's life depends upon the skill and ability to manage one's thoughts because as Emerson wrote: *"The ancestor of every action is a thought."*

Extremely rapid changes in human behavior have been achieved with the application of NLP methodology. The effectiveness and rapidity of these changes are bringing the tenets of traditional therapy and psychiatry into serious question. It is a credit to the genius of Richard Bandler that he has refused to be content with the great achievements thus far realized in this new science of the mind.

He continues to develop new patterns or models of behavior by weeding out "what doesn't work" and refining what does. In fact, if you want to see great entertainment, you should watch Bandler's outrageous humor pulverize any symbol of smug complacency. His work is a testimony to the fact that the brain is a machine without an "off" switch and can be directed to generate or create infinite patterns for excellence and resourceful living.

Richard Bandler's discovery of the application of submodalities, that is the fine distinctions of the modalities of the five representational channels, has imbued behavior change work with a quantum leap in power and elegance. I have maintained that until a better book comes along, Bandler's book, "Using Your Brain For A Change," is excellent information for all who want to run their own brains.

A basic principle taught in NLP is that in the process of thought, the brain codes information using three major Representational (coding) Systems—visual pictures, auditory sounds, and kinesthetic feelings. The sequence in which these are arranged (the syntax) is what determines their meaning to us. During communication, one's internal thought processes can be followed by paying attention to the representational system being accessed.

Every human being's model of the world or point of view of the world is described by his/her representational systems and the arrangements of these. The sequence in which individuals engage these systems describes how they think. To understand an individual and to communicate effectively with him, one must first enter his model of the world by observing his representational systems during communication. People tend to favor one representational system over the others and so we generally speak of one's Primary Representational System type. A person can be classified as being primarily a visual type, an auditory type or a kinesthetic type of individual. A visual type of individual experiences the world primarily through pictures. This individual is bound to be different and behave differently from someone else who interprets the world through sounds, that is, the auditory type, or through feelings–the

71

kinesthetic type. Most people tend to habitually favor one representational system over the others. Everyone blends all three systems for their total expression of experience.

How do we recognize the representational types? The quickest indicator of the representational system in play is the eye accessing cue. Eye movements are used to stimulate the brain to access the particular representational system with which one is processing information. Eye accessing cues can be viewed as catalysts which trigger appropriate areas of the brain to access pictures, words or feelings. By watching eye movements, we can tell which representational system is being engaged.

The eye accessing cues are an involuntary action—an unconscious response.

Please note that the following description of the eye cues as movement right and left apply only to right-handed people. For left-handed people, the right and left movements are reversed.

EYE ACCESSING CUES

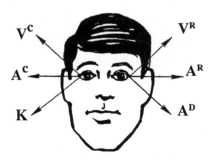

Right Side   **Left Side**

V^R - Visual Remembered Images:
These are images of things seen before and recalled in the way they were originally seen. Example: Describe your bedroom.

V^C - Visual Constructed Images:
Seeing images or pictures of things one has not seen before.

72

Example: What would you look like if you had a tail?

A^R - Auditory Remembered Sounds:
Remembering words and sounds heard before. Example: What does your lover's voice sound like?

A^C - Auditory Construct:
Making up sounds never heard before or never heard exactly the same way. Example: Imagine cats singing Jingle Bells .

A^D - Auditory Digital:
Having internal dialogue. Also seeking meaning or making sense.

K - Kinesthetic:
Feeling tactile sensation of touch, body movements and feeling emotions. Example: What does diving feel like? Describe the feelings of ecstasy.

The Representational Systems

Thought is the human being's focus on the world. As I have said, this focus or viewpoint consists of an infinite sequence of representational accesses.

We interact with the world around us by continuously using all our sensory channels for:

* Seeing pictures outside and remembering or constructing pictures inside our heads.

* Listening to sounds, remembering or imagining how things would sound and making sense out of it.

* Feeling sensations and remembering the feelings or constructing them.

* Engaging our sense of smell and taste actively or remembering or constructing tastes and smells.

These are modified and coded in the brain in sequences that are specific to each individual. The sequence of coding these representations is known as strategy, and it is what determines how we do what we do or our behavior. The key to gaining entrance into a person's world, their point of view of the world is through eliciting and utilizing their strategy. This is done by observing how they access each representational system using the eye accessing cues, and by listening to their language patterns.

Visual Representational System

It is estimated that about 45 percent of members in this society code information predominantly through the visual system. Visual external is simply seeing pictures in the world. The visual channel is a very fast way of recording information because large chunks of it can be taken in with each blink of the eye.

We see by using our eyes to track large fields of vision or by focusing on details of information within a given visual field. In other words, we see contextually, or we focus on details of the contents in a visual field. Some individuals are habitually contextual viewers; others prefer to focus on the richness of details. Most people do a combination of detailed viewing and contextual scanning, depending on the results they wish to achieve. In general, contextual vision is useful for storing the entire picture, but scanning details is good for storing the finer points of information in a picture.

Right Side   **Left side**

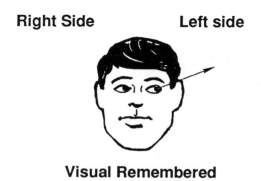

Visual Remembered

When right-handed people are remembering a visual image, the direction of eye movement is up and to the left. Ask these people a question that involves remembering an image such as: "What color was the dress you wore yesterday?" "They may say," Well, let's see," and their eyes will move upwards to the left.

People will normally recall images in the manner they were stored. When people claim that they cannot see pictures in their minds, it often means that they are unable to remember the details of the pictures. It may also mean that they have forgotten the particular picture they saw because they did not pay much conscious attention to it in the first place. Nonetheless, they did store the visual experience unconsciously.

Right Side   **Left Side**

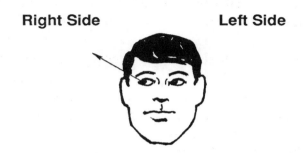

Visual Construct

The ability to construct images not previously seen is the key to genius. Our greatest scientists possess an uncanny ability to construct visual images in the space screen of their imagination. Albert Einstein constructed a picture of himself riding on the head of a light beam traveling through space. Out of that vision was born the theory of relativity. Nicola Tesla, who is perhaps the greatest inventor of all time, had a legendary ability to construct inventions in his imagination with great precision. (See chapter on Mind Magic.)

Visual construct is important in education because information can be easily remembered by making pictures of it. To do mathematics well, it is very important that one has the ability to do visual construct. This is also true of reading. In reading and story telling, we construct a movie in our heads while scanning over words or listening to the story. Unfortunately, our children are taught to pronounce words while reading. Even more disastrous is the effect of television on the ability to do visual construct. Television provides our children with pictures that are already constructed. They don't have to do visual construct and so we are becoming a society with a rapidly diminishing ability to do visual construct. This erodes the richness of the imagination, a quality that was key to the development and growth of this country. Is it any wonder that the mathematic skills of United States children have diminished in recent years? If we are going to continue to encourage genius, our educational system will have to pay attention to the development of the imagination and visual construct.

Auditory Representational System

About 15 percent of the members of this society are thought to favor the auditory representation system predominantly in coding information. We evaluate what we hear either by how it sounds—auditory tonal, or whether it sounds meaningful or makes sense—auditory digital.

Right Side   **Left Side**

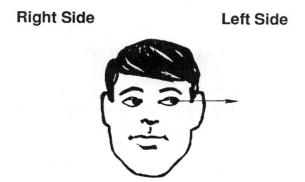

Auditory Remembered

Also, as with the visual representation system, people hear sounds in details or contextually. The detail listener prefers to listen to one sound at a time. The contextual listener pays attention only to the tone and mood generated by the sounds. How things sound is more important that what is said to this individual.

Auditory Remembered means remembering what something sounds like. Musician's are adept at remembering sounds. People who are capable of speaking many languages usually do so because they can store and recall each language in its own tone and tempo.

Right Side   **Left Side**

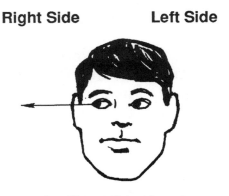

Auditory Construct

Auditory construct is the area where the great composers and orators excel. These musicians are adept at constructing sounds or combinations of sounds never heard before. The orators put thoughts into words they construct auditorally.

Confusion arises when certain individuals are observed to be engaged in quick repetitive patterns of eye scanning from auditory remembered to auditory construct positions, during conversation. What is happening here? These individuals are using a strategy which consists of hearing constructed or unfamiliar auditory information and then checking them against data banks of remembered auditory sounds. In other words, they are checking how they are sounding. They are not "shifty eyed" as they may have been accused.

Right Side   **Left Side**

Auditory Digital

When we are making decisions or evaluating what we heard, we often use internal dialogue. Internal dialogue is simply talking to oneself. It is thought that everyone engages in internal dialogue all the time without being conscious of it. People become conscious of their internal dialogue mostly when they judge it as a limitation that interferes with their outcomes such as during meditation.

The auditory digital is what we use to seek meaning or make sense out of what we say to ourselves. We are in effect listening to ourselves to evaluate if a thing sounds right or makes sense.

Kinesthetic Representational System

Right Side   **Left Side**

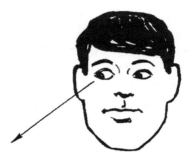

Kinesthetic (also Olfactory and Gustatory)

The single direction of eye movement—down and to the right, presents the kinesthetic accessing cues. Also both the gustatory and olfactory accessing cues are represented by this type of eye movement.

About 40 percent of our population code information primarily through the kinesthetic presentation. Kinesthetic consists of external and internal sensations and feelings. Great athletes have a special ability to pay attention to body sensations during training and to recall and duplicate these sensations at will.

The ability to code and store body sensation associated with the effects of drugs and to recall these at will may create a new milestone in medicine. It will be a worthwhile challenge to train people to control their autonomic system functions as well as the functioning of other body systems at will. We will then be on our way to creating a new breed of superhumans if we can manipulate our physiologic functions at will.

Olfactory and Gustatory Representational System

The olfactory representational system is rarely mentioned and yet odors are very important in affecting moods. The olfactory (smell) organs are located immediately adjacent to the deepest and most primitive part of the brain. Of all the sensations, smell alone has a direct connection to the nervous system. All others are mediated through the cerebral cortex. Smell, therefore, has a direct and rapid effect on our behavior and its effects are quite unconscious.

Positive smells of which people are not consciously aware can put them in excellent states of emotion. Herein lies the success of the billion dollar perfume industry. Cleaning up air pollution may generate valuable human resources by freeing us from constant bombardment of noxious fumes which increases stress.

The gustatory, or sense of taste, is a contact sense, mediated through the mouth and tongue. It consists of the following sensations: bitter, sweet, sour and salty. These sensations can be remembered or constructed. Great cooks have highly developed this system.

Language patterns of people correlate to a high degree with their primary representational systems. How we use words to say something about a subject or an idea, that is, the predicates we use, describe our dominant coding system at the time. This is no surprise since our words are intimately bonded to our thoughts. Here are some examples of verbal pattern/predicates of the major representation system types:

Visual	Auditory	Kinesthetic
see	listen	touch
glimpse	ring	feel
view	hear	stroke
retrospect	talk	handle
foggy	discuss	sense
clear	echo	impact

To illustrate the use of these predicates in expression, a visual person may express his understanding of an idea by saying, "I see what you mean," while an auditory person may say, "It rings true to me," and a kinesthetic individual expresses the same by saying, "It feels right to me."

In classifying people according to their dominant representational coding system, we must always be aware that we are creating limitations in our understanding of thought functioning because all our sensory channels are in operation all the time. We only become aware of the channel with which we are focusing our attention at any given moment.

For example, as I sit in my back yard on a cool, clear desert morning writing this, I am fully engaged in thinking and jotting things down on a yellow pad. But is that all I'm doing really? No. As I relax, I recognize that I am aware of a soft cool breeze on my skin and I hear the chirping of birds and the distant roar of a jet plane. Each time I blink my eyes, I see the picture of the garden, the red, yellow, purple, orange and white colors of the flowers against the backdrop of the green grass and the palm trees. I see the hummingbirds dancing in mid-air. I also get a whiff of the aroma of jasmine on the trellis. And even though I am seriously busy writing now about metamedicine, I am aware of my internal dialogue which says, "How very beautiful."

We engage all our representational systems in processing experience at each given moment in time. It is only because in consciousness we recognize this coding (thought) process as appearing to occur one system at a time, in a linear time frame, that it seems as if we are engaging only one system or the other. When we do this, the representational or coding system in conscious awareness becomes the dominant representational type at the time. The others, including all the information they contain, are relegated to the unconscious part of the mind, that is, everything we are not aware of. It is easy then to appreciate what a powerful storehouse of information the unconscious mind is and how much potential is available outside of conscious awareness.

Characteristics of the Representational Types

The visual representational types code information by relying mostly on sight or imagery. Since seeing is a very rapid process of gathering sensory data, these individuals seem to have a fast voice tempo and breathe high in their chest. They use visual expressions and language.

The auditory types are the musicians of our population. How things sound and the rhythm or pitch are very important in thought processing to these individuals. They trust sounds. They talk to themselves in internal dialogue and they love talk. These people breathe in the middle of their chest and their voices are pleasing to them.

The kinesthetic types rely on feeling: touch externally and emotion internally, to make sense out of reality. They breathe lower, in the abdomen. Their speech is slower than the other two types because they take time to check out their feelings in order to verbalize their thoughts. They have easier access to their emotions and so are regarded as very sensitive people.

The typing of people as visual, auditory, and kinesthetic types, although very limiting is nevertheless useful for recognizing what the dominant thought patterns are. This affords us an access to the window of one's perception of the world or one's mentality. Any attempt to restrict one's self to one coding mode or to exclusively use one representational system in the process of thinking will result in restriction of the expression of the self.

We can expand our perception of the world by processing information through all representational systems. This gives us more choices and therefore, more power in any given circumstance.

By paying attention to thought processes, the sequencing of representations and language patterns, we can detect the strategy which when followed, produces a specific behavior in people. To illustrate, a grossly obese patient was referred to my metamedicine weight control clinic because she had successfully defeated every weight reduction method devised within recent memory. She stated as her major outcome that she would like to feel good when she meets new people. I urged her to tell me what usually happens when she meets new people.

"Well," she began, and her eyes looked up to the left, "they look at me." Then her eyes looked horizontally to the right, "And I know what they are saying—that I am disgusting," she continued. Then her eyes looked down to her right. She gazed straight ahead momentarily with defocused eyes, and then she looked down again to her right saying, "and I know they are right."

Her eye accessing cues revealed this patient's thought processes when she met new people. She sees them or remembers seeing them. Then, in her imagination, she hears them saying that she is disgusting, and she gets a negative feeling. She then checks this by picturing herself and she goes back to her negative feelings. Her feelings are all she is usually aware of whenever she thinks of meeting new people. Her basic strategy is Vr-Ac-K, i.e. visual recall-auditory construct-kinesthetic. In this strategy, she begins by *leading* visually. She constructs auditorally. She *represents* kinesthetically and has a visual *reference* check system that she uses to confirm that her feelings are valid. Our reference system is how we decide whether what we have accessed in consciousness is true or not. By interrupting this sequence, she eliminated the problem with meeting new people.

Knowing a person's strategy not only allows you to help him/her eliminate a limitation, but it can also become a useful tool for leading them to useful behaviors. One person's successful strategy for a specific task can be learned or installed in other people. This idea of modeling useful strategies has been used to great advantage in sports training and it can be of tremendous value in education. Take spelling as an example. It was recognized that good spellers have a two step strategy. They visualize the word that they spell and they check kinesthetically for accuracy by getting a feeling for it at the midline of the torso. If all children are taught this, no one will have trouble spelling. Instead, we are taught early on to "sound out words" auditorally.

Words form the content of thought. What are words? They are simply symbols for ideas. Just as a map is not the territory it represents, the word is not the thing named. It is just a mass-agreed upon symbol or sound for the idea of the thing being named. Words are combined to form language. Words and language are the symbolic vehicles humans use to express thought.

Because each idea is understood or perceived by each person from his/her viewpoint (filtered version), it becomes a necessity to find out what another human being really means by his communication.

Bandler and Grinder have developed a precision model for communication. In NLP teaching, the precision model has been ingeniously simplified and reduced to five questions. Referred to as the five Pointers, these questions lead to specific concrete sensory-based information. Imagine that I walked up to you and told you, "He hurt me." In order for you to understand clearly what I meant, you would have to know who "he" refers to and how specifically I was "hurt".

For accelerated learning and pragmatic application, the five Pointers are arranged on the fingers of the hand.

On the fingers of one hand are arranged the Pointers. The fingers of the opposite hand contain the questions designed to clarfiy the Pointers. (See diagram next page.)

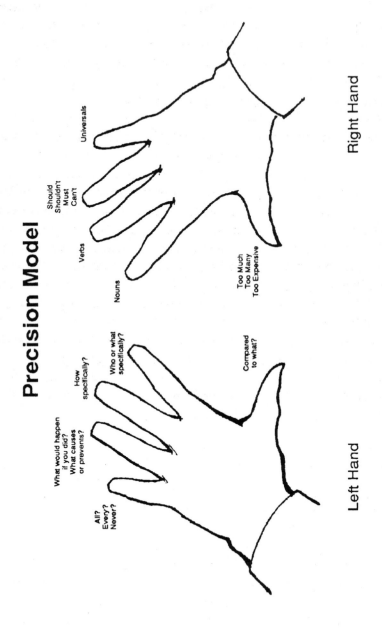

Precision Model

Right Hand

Left Hand

Universals

Should
Shouldn't
Must
Can't

Verbs

Nouns

Too Much
Too Many
Too Expensive

What would happen
if you did?
What causes
or prevents?

How
specifically?

Who or what
specifically?

Compared
to what?

All?
Every?
Never?

Left Thumb

Right Thumb

<u>Left Hand</u>
Compared to what?

<u>Right Hand</u>
too much
too many
too expensive

Sample Statement:

This book is too expensive.
Metamedicine takes too much concentration.

Precision Generator:

Maintain rapport, integrity and curiosity while you ask:
Compared to what?

Left Index   Right Index

 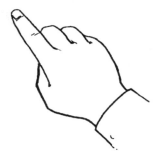

Left Hand   Right Hand

Who or what specifically   Nouns
Who says? For whom?

Sample Statement:

They don't like me.
It is difficult to make changes.

Precision Generator:

Maintain rapport, integrity and curiosity while you ask:
Who specifically does not like you?
Who says it is difficult to make changes?
For whom is it difficult to make changes

Left Middle Finger   Right Middle Finger

 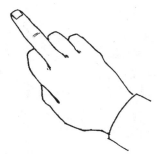

Left Hand   Right Hand

How specifically   Verbs

Sample Statement:

> My job irritates me.

Precision Generator:

> Maintain rapport, integrity and curiosity while you ask:
> How specifically does your job irritate you?

Left 4th Finger   ## Right 4th Finger

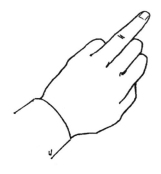 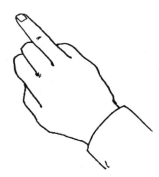

Left Hand

What would happen of you did?
What prevents?
What causes?

Right Hand

should   shouldn't
must   will not
can   can't
have to

Sample Statement:

> I shouldn't be this bold.
> I can't learn a new language.

Precision Generator:

> Maintain rapport, integrity and curiosity while you ask:
>> What would happen if you did?
>> What prevents you from learning a new language?

Left 5th Finger   Right 5th Finger

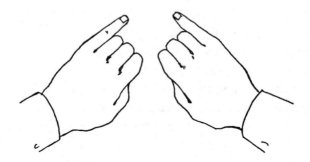

Left Hand   ### Right Hand

All?   Universals
Every?
Never?

Sample Statement:

I never get any respect.

Precision Generator:

While maintaining rapport, integrity, and curiosity ask:
Never? Has anyone ever shown you respect?

On the right hand, the first Pointer—the nonspecific nouns are placed on the index finger. The second Pointer - the nonspecific verbs go on the middle finger. The third Pointer - rules like should, shouldn't, must, and can't are placed on the ring finger. The fourth Pointer - generalizations or universals go on the fifth finger: all, every and never. The fifth Pointer is for changing comparators without antecedents, such as: better, too much, too many, and too expensive. These are placed on the thumb.

The matching fingers of the opposite hand contain the questions. Thus to the unspecified nouns, the question on the left index finger is: who or what specifically? On the left middle finger, the question to the unspecified verbs is: how specifically? On the left ring finger, the matching questions to the rules are: what would happen if? and what causes or prevents? On the fifth finger, the questions to generalizations are: all? every? never?

Used with skill, while maintaining rapport, the Pointers can open the door to the contents of another person's thoughts to us. It keeps us from acting from the illusion that other people's words have the same meaning for them as they have for us.

In the following sections of this work, we shall explore how the three components of our personality makeup—belief, emotionality, and mentality blend together to generate the drama we experience as the events of our lives, including disease.

Of the three aspects of the persona, we have described mentality or thought as being our operational mode in conscious awareness. We quite often personalize mentality or thought and call it the ego. It is the rational, analytical part of us with which we make changes in our emotions and belief. Of the three aspects of our personality, belief is the most remote from conscious awareness. We are generally not aware of most of our beliefs. They can be so hidden in the deepest recesses of the mind that most people think that beliefs are impossible to change. Beliefs can be changed easily once we uncover or identify them because we acquire most of our beliefs without being aware of doing so. As children, we literally absorb the beliefs of those closest to us: our parents, our family members and our peers. We accept and encode these beliefs because we must trust our parents and peers in order to survive. Our rational analytical thought processes do not seem to be focused enough at this stage to assume its protective questioning function. Unfortunately, through the habit of negativity in most cultures of the world, the individuals born to our societies acquire early, a core belief system steeped in negativity.

The task of metamedicine in the treatment of illness is to uncover the core negative beliefs, which underlie the illness, and to change them by using the thought processes to install more resourceful beliefs in their place. This is the source of the power of metamedicine in using disease to create a more successful and joyous life.

Using the knowledge of what thought is and how it works, we are now equipped to use this universal tool to create a superior life on earth by redefining and eliminating disease.

Before illustrating how disease is not only healed but used to propel an individual into a superior life experience, it is important that we view and understand the disease process from metamedicine's point of view.

6
Metamedicine Model of Disease Process

"Suffering was the only thing
Made me feel that I am alive."
-Popular song

Most adults notice their bodies only when they have pain. Enjoyment of a healthy body is a concept very foreign to most human beings all over the world. We expect to suffer. Even in athletics, where the optimum power of the human spirit and body are expressed and celebrated, the favorite saying or belief is: "no pain, no gain."

Are you beginning to perceive how deeply negativity resonates through the human mind? This cycle of negativity has gone on for thousands of years of human existence. If you doubt it, check the history books. Therefore, when I say that human beings use disease as a tool for learning and you ask why, remember our habit of negativity. Negative beings will have a tendency to use negative tools until they are sick and tired of it. Then, they may prefer to change and use positive tools to accomplish the same results. However, as long as we are going to continue to use disease, let's make the most of it.

We now know that we are creatures of choice and that we

become self-empowered once we accept responsibility for this choice and the applications of it. Let us examine what an illness is, so that we can get a handle on it, understand it and empower ourselves to use it to tune in to a more joyous life. Here is my favorite definition of an illness: an illness is a symptom of a *dis*-ease in the persona.

Take a look at the following true story. Among the friends I made at a local jogging trail was a vivacious woman in her late thirties whom I will call Eva. Quite often I would run a mile with her, exchanging pleasantries and I would usually excuse myself and speed off, because in those days I disliked talking while running. Gradually, Eva got me to slow down and chat a little more on the trail. To my surprise, I found that I enjoyed this.

One day, I found Eva walking instead of running and I stopped to ask if she had suffered an injury.

"Oh, it's my back," she explained. "It is killing me!"

"Have you gone to see any doctor about this?" I asked.

"Yes," she answered wearily. "I went to the orthopedic surgeon and he ordered me to have bedrest."

"Then why are you out here walking?"

"I need to get away from my kids," she explained. "They are driving me crazy."

"Teenage trouble?" I surmised.

"Yeah, I wish they'd get off my back," she sighed .

After this, I didn't see Eva for many weeks. One evening in late spring I ran into her in her neighborhood. I was shocked at what I saw. She was emaciated and walked with a cane. A pinched expression had replaced the joy that she used to radiate. It was as if she had turned into an old woman overnight. She told me that she had gone through back surgery. I asked if she was in much physical pain and she said no. She told me that her family had rallied to help her following her surgery. I encouraged her to keep walking and to concentrate on achieving full recovery while distancing herself from all worry. Weeks later she was able to take regular walks without a cane.

About one year later I ran into Eva during an early morning run and asked her how she was doing.

"Life's a bitch," she declared. "Everything is going wrong. I've got several relatives hospitalized and I can't stand my new job and ..."

"And your back is hurting again," I added. She stopped suddenly and stared at me.

"How did you know?" she asked surprised. "I mean, how did you know about my back?"

"Come now, Eva. Give your back a rest," I cajoled. "Get the load off your back." We walked silently for a few yards, then she stopped and grabbed my right shoulder.

"You are absolutely right, Vida . I need to take it easy," she admitted. "I can't carry everybody's burden."

"Of course not," I agreed. "And if you do, your back will cave in. Besides, don't you respect other people enough to let them handle their own problems?"

"You're right," she said nodding. "My worrying about them isn't helping them any."

"What about your new job? What are you going to do about it?"

"Oh, ... that," she said frowning. "I think I'll quit it and see if I can find something I like."

"That's the spirit!" I declared, cheering her on.

She hugged me and I read a message of profound gratitude in her embrace. A few weeks later I met her again and she was a woman transformed. It was obvious that she was again enjoying life. She had beaten her back problem. Had she never had a chance to discover what the disease of her "back illness" was all about and healed it, she would probably have continued to have back surgery. Each surgery would have been temporarily successful in providing her relief from the illness. Eventually, no surgeon would agree to operate on her back and she would be labeled a "chronic backer." Her doctors and therapists, frustrated at failing in providing her with lasting relief would have bounced her from one pain clinic to another. And when she is inevitably bounced back to her original doctor, he would literally duck under the desk and invent a very creative excuse for not being able to see her. It is to Eva's credit that she took control of her disease and circumvented what would have been a horror story.

Now, was Eva's back disorder or illness real? Of course it was. There was pathology in her vertebrae and sophisticated radiologic studies confirmed this. Otherwise, the orthopedic surgeon would not have advised surgery. What caused the pathology, the disorder in her back bones? Well, we could write volumes on the usual medical scenario, going through from family history, genetic predisposition and possible past and current injuries. But the fact remains that it was Eva and not anybody else with a similar predisposition, who suffered the back disorder. Why her? Because it was her choice. Suspend your judgement for a moment while we work through this idea. She obviously did not make this choice consciously. A doctor or anyone with a working knowledge of metamedicine can get access into her world—her internal thought processes and alert her to this unconscious choice.

Let us pause and take a look at the definition of disease again.

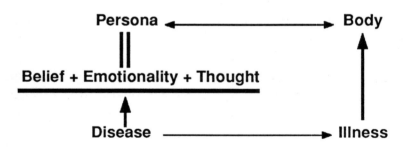

Disease is just what it says—*dis*-ease. It means that the persona or the personality is not at ease with all that it is. Again, the personality is made up of beliefs, emotionality and mentality or thought. Anything that interferes with the ease of expression of this triad of the personality prism will be reflected in the body as a disease or what we know as an illness.

As a review of the persona composition, recall that belief is the blueprint of what we experience in life. It is the primary basal level of the persona make-up triad and comes before emotion. Recall also that emotion has been described as an energy reaction to a belief. It is the energy that activates belief towards physical manifestation. Emotion comes before thought or mentality. This is why our feelings or emotions quite often seem irrational, because even though we may thoroughly understand an idea, our feelings about it may remain out of touch with reason. As an example, a husband may have proof that his wife is faithful, but he still has feelings of jealousy, which are definitely negative emotions, whenever she smiles at another man. He cannot explain his jealousy because emotion is not subject to reason, rationality or thought. He would have to make changes in his emotions to stop feeling jealous. Underlying this emotion is a belief that he is undeserving and therefore, he can't have his wife's undivided affection. The emotions of jealousy are then a reaction to this belief.

Now, let's get back to Eva's case history. Her language is fairly explicit about the disease in her persona. Generally, there are no mistakes in human communication, because language describes what goes on in the brain. We learn that: she has back problems; there are problems with her children and she is having an emotional reaction to them.

"They are driving me crazy," she had said. She stated, "I wish they'd get off my back."

What Eva lets us glimpse of her world from her description is the following:

She is having an emotional reaction, which she feels as a burden on her back. Why the emotional *dis*-ease? Remember that an emotion is a reaction to a belief. What is her belief in this instance? Let's check what she is experiencing in her body because that will give us the clues to her blueprint or beliefs. The support structure of her body, her back bone is disintegrating. Metaphorically, one can say that her back is being weighed down by a burden. We begin to get the idea that she has a belief that she must carry other people's burdens. Whether she is aware that she has or has not bought into such a belief does not matter. The crucial thing is that she contains such a belief because that is what she is manifesting.

Her actual illness, the anatomical disorder in her back bones, was cured with surgery and physical therapy. That initial back illness was a symptom of the actual disease which is the larger picture or the larger issue. The illness, which is really only a symptom, was cured but was healing of the disease achieved? No. For a while, Eva's back was okay. Then, other members of her family became hospitalized and she proceeded to assume their burden, thereby activating a negative emotional response again. That she began to experience back problems again was a foregone conclusion.

Once I pointed out to her that she could choose to let other people handle their own problems, she made a shift and stopped buying into other people's problems. In other words, she redesigned her blueprint and left out the part about being the family mule.

With a change in belief she had achieved a healing of the disease at the basal level. In working on a job that excited her, she was aligning herself with her signature vibratory energy or emotion for her fullest self expression. The fullest expression of the self means living the life you must live in order to be the best possible human being you can be. In other words, it is being clearly who you are meant to be.

In metamedicine when we encounter an illness, we use it as a cue to discover the *dis*-ease because every illness is a result of disease in the mind first, before it is manifested in the body. We use our medical skills to cure the body while we guide the person with the disease in healing his/her life. It is in the sense of allowing the individual to regain the capacity for full expression of the self that the meaning of health truly becomes the absence of disease.

If all disease means is a lack of ease at the foundations of the personality, how come there are so many diseases? This is a question I am often asked and sometimes, after a gut level consideration, I have to be honest and say, "We have to have a lot of diseases so that the world won't be terrorized by roving bands of starving doctors."

All right, seriously now, humans manifest diseases in so many forms of illnesses because each individual is a unique viewpoint, a unique expression. In other words, individuals perceive the world differently according to their unique thought patterns. So they have the capacity to express the basic idea of disease in many forms in line with their signature thought forms and emotional vibratory energy. Which individuals develop what type of diseases has been a facinating area of study for both the medical profession and the public at large. I am not immune from this fascination with who develops what disease and for what reason. I wrote a fictional work along these lines, "Metamed. AIDS: Rousing the gods," to explore my ideas on the AIDS epidemic.

In the section of this book on emotion, I discussed briefly the grouping of individuals according to their habitual emotional display and the disease these groups are prone to suffer. For a while, the controversy over the existence of the Type A behavioral individuals and what diseases fall into their particular domain kept the medical establishment entertained. If we must group and label people according to the diseases they are prone to employ, it may be more useful to view them in terms of personal power.

To review, there are diseases of those who do not trust their power. These individuals strive to gain power over themselves and others in order to feel powerful. They do not believe that they are powerful enough to have anything that they desire without hurting themselves or others. These people's favorite diseases are hypertension, cardiac disease, gastrointestinal diseases and headaches.

Then, there is the group of individuals who refuse to acknowledge that they have any power at all. These people deny their power and refuse to take any responsibility for it. They exhibit hopelessness and helplessness. As they abandon themselves to despair, their bodies' immune system abandon the barriers they put up against invasion by infection causing organisms. So, we find that these individuals are prone to immune system related diseases like rheumatoid arthritis, etc. They are also fond of cancers, another disease characterized by lack of control at the cellular level.

Between these two extremes range various gradations of personality types and their indigenous diseases. Ultimately, it must be recognized that diseases result from negative elements in one or more of the three aspects of the persona construct. In the first place, the three elements of the personality or persona construct are what give rise to behavior. Every behavior a human exhibits has as its source either his/her belief, emotion or thought. It can also come from all of these or a combination of the three.

Diseases are strictly personal affairs. They are custom-made, you might say. Even when the diseases are diagnosed to be the same, each individual experiences the illness in a different way. As medical practicioners, we learn early that the classical symptoms and signs of a given disease are nothing more than an average of the presenting symptoms exhibited by our patients. Rarely, if ever, do we see a "text book" case of anything. Each person's disease occurs for a specific purpose which is related to the path that he/ she has chosen to walk in this life. What is this path? The path is a metaphor that represents the life one must live to become the best possible human being she/he can be in this world. An individual who is living this way can be described as achieving full expression of the self.

_The metamedicine weight control program, which we run at our outpatient surgery center, confirms that the real disease is different for each person suffering from the same illness. The illness or symptomatology involved here is obesity. Each participant has more than double the acceptable percentage of body fat for their sex, age, and activity levels. The participants are allowed to enroll in the program after they have exhausted most of the current weight loss measures and failed to achieve permanent weight loss. Their typical history is cycles of weight loss on a restrictive diet regimen which is followed by weight gain, quite often in excess of the weight lost once the individual stops the diet regimen. All participants are required to agree in writing to take full responsibility for their progress and results. This last measure is their declaration of self-empowerment.

After the initial complete physical examination, we take them through the first Metamedicine sessions. In the initial Metamed session, we enter the patient's world to discover with them what the disease is about. As soon as we get through existing emotional barriers, we go to the belief system and make appropriate changes. Once the negative beliefs involved (blueprints) are changed, the entire picture changes. The individual has now created him/herself to be a person who no longer has a weight control problem. The actual weight loss that follows is only a by-product of the positive changes in the personality and lifestyle that results.

The simplest disease I have encountered in the program is a negative belief that depicts middle age as the end of energetic life. A typical example is a man I recently interacted with. This individual practically set the rheostat of his (emotional) energy to zero. His major complaint was lack of energy. He stated that he would sleep all day if he was allowed. With only a change of belief, his enthusiasm for life soared and he was losing weight at the rate of one pound per day.

The most pitiful disease we encountered in the metamedicine weight control program, was that of a woman who suffered from the disease of guilt. Please recognize that hate is not the opposite of love. Guilt is the opposite of love. Guilt is the feeling of total nondeservability of love. With hate, one still acknowledges that one is deserving except that she/he goes about it in a negative way. The emotion of hate results from a knowledge of self-worth that is for some reason, thwarted or denied. With the disease of guilt, this individual believed that she was unworthy of love and her emotional (energy) make-up was totally negative. She was incapable of recalling any positive feelings or positive events in her life. Interestingly, her idea of herself and of her life was that of an amorphous mass. Her eating binges only served to reinforce her total denial of power and abandonment of control. Recall that love is the highest emotion, the highest energy level. She did not enjoy eating, it was just one of the various activities in her life that reflected her total and hopeless negativity. It was her belief in the existence of God that gave us the first breakthrough to her world in order to make the changes that were vital in this case.

The one common element I found in the disease of each participant in the metamed weight control program is the degree of self-rejection. Could it be that lack of self-acceptance underlies this sort of disorder? This would be an interesting subject for study.

As I have stated, the most effective way to heal a disease in the person is to deal with the core of the problem, the negative belief system. I have described some of the ways we uncover what the causative negative beliefs are. However, most people continue to wonder what the source of these undesirable beliefs is. I also wondered about this and still search for the answer each time I find that I have to change yet another belief in order to rid myself of a miserable circumstance. Where do these negative beliefs come from?

Young children and babies are very sensitive to the emotional energy of their environment. They naturally absorb the beliefs and fears of people around them, especially those of their parents, whom they must trust implicitly in order to survive. When a child is fed a steady diet of doubt and fears, a strong negative belief system becomes a foundation for his/her experience in life. When a child grows up hearing or picking up on the following attitudes: "Life is tough; only the rich can succeed; you are not smart enough; you are not pretty enough; you must pay your dues to get anything worth-while, etc., etc.," a child views the world through lenses clouded with fear and doubt. Is it any wonder then that this child will experience a life of struggle and disease?

Please note that fear is belief in the negative and doubt is trust in negative beliefs. People will manifest either that which they believe or that which they fear. Belief and fear form the blueprints of the reality we experience, fear being the total opposite of belief.

The negative belief systems which we form early in life as the result of living in civilizations steeped in habitual negativity remain with us and unconsciously become the source of the negative events we suffer. As we grow into adulthood, we learn to judge and pick up the judgements of other people around us, especially those of our peers and authority figures. Consider the following events:

When I was a child in primary school, a group of children were having difficulty with mathematics. Our teacher, a loving wise man, told them that if they could stay after school he would tell them the secret of being good at math. That got their curiosity up and they couldn't wait until after the "school over" bell rang.

"Math is easy," he whispered after peeking at the closed door as if to assure that they were all alone with him .

"It is just a game," he continued. "All you have to do is learn the rules and pay attention very carefully—very carefully." Then, he took them through addition and subtraction, substituting farm animals and vegetables for the numbers. It was such great fun.

In another classroom of second graders, my friend Ifeoma was one of a group of children detained after school because they had failed their math test. Her teacher told them that they were poor in math, and in her own words, "punished us by making us do pages of math work." For the rest of our school days Ifeoma avoided any classes that required mathematics. She believed that she had no ability in it. My friends in the first group took on all math classes in those days as a challenge to find out how really good they could get because they believed that math was just a game.

I see quite a few young men and women at our outpatient clinics who suffer from high blood pressure. Most of them tell me that they are not surprised to discover that they had hypertension. On questioning them, I hear the same explanations most of the time: They had been told that hypertension ran in their family. They believed that it was just a matter of time before they developed hypertension. One young woman in her twenties had been suffering from hypertension off and on for a few years. Her physician would intermittently put her on antihypertensive drugs to control the high blood pressure. Her pressure would fall below normal and he would have her discontinue the drugs. At an interview she told me this: "I always knew that it was just a matter of time before I would have high blood pressure. My grandmother said that all the women in my family are supposed to get it."

I looked her in the eye, raised an eyebrow and asked, "Didn't she tell you that you are not supposed to get it until you are a very old woman?"

After that, her pressures stayed normal. Such is the power of doubt. The smallest doubt will undermine anybody's belief system. All I did was sow a little seed of doubt in the belief she bought from her grandmother.

As adults, we can pick up beliefs or buy into belief unwittingly. Recently, a young woman called Elaine, whose kidney transplant had failed, was sent to my husband who is a vascular surgeon, for construction of a vascular access for dialysis. I was this patient's anesthesiologist during the procedure. I became interested in her and asked her if she would prefer not to depend upon the dialysis machines for the rest of her life. She gave me a strange look, smiled and said, "Yes, Doctor, but how can I do that?" I invited her to a metamedicine session.

I spent some time gaining access to her world by letting her ramble on about her life, and I learned a great deal about her. Apparently, she suffered kidney failure during a tragic pregnancy and was put on dialysis. Shortly after that she was fortunate to receive a kidney from a donor and she had a kidney transplant. Seven years later this kidney also showed signs of failure, and that was the point that we got involved with her—constructing the vascular access for dialysis which was to follow.

I had her go through the details of the circumstances involving the original renal failure and transplant. One of the incidents she described to me occurred on the day before she was to receive her kidney transplant. She related that she had gone down to the hospital laboratory for blood tests. On her way back to her room from the lab, she rode up in the elevator with an older woman in a wheelchair. The woman asked what she was in the hospital for and she said she was there to receive a kidney transplant.

106

"Oh, I had a kidney transplant once," the woman told her. "It failed after seven years." Elaine paused and stared at the floor.

"And what did you feel about that, Elaine?" I asked.

"You know, it is funny, Doctor," she said, curiosity narrowing her eyes, "Since that time, there is this thing about seven years— seven years just keeps coming back to me. I keep hearing myself saying 'seven years.'"

"How long did you think that your kidney was going to last?" I asked her abruptly.

"I didn't know how long it would last—I didn't ask the doctor," she answered haltingly.

"What did you tell yourself about how long you could keep it?" I persisted.

"Well I said I'd probably have it for seven years," Elaine said and shrugged. "Five years, maybe ... yes, seven years tops."

I reviewed the details of her renal transplant surgery and the time when she began noticing signs of kidney failure. It was exactly seven years!

I reviewed her medical records and found out that the transplanted kidney was intact; she was still putting out adequate quantities of urine. However, it was failing in its function of doing adequate filtration of by-products of normal body metabolism. Therefore, in the metamedicine session, I did belief change with her and took her through Time Line therapy work. We co-designed a meditation that reinforced her resources. Then, I urged that her blood laboratory studies be repeated in one week.

One week later, when I saw her again, she was vivacious. She jubilantly reported that her creatinine level (an important indicator of renal function) had mysteriously improved and that she had never felt so energetic. The last time I saw her, she had gained weight, and she told me she was planning on getting a job and buying a house. She raised her forearm, pointed at the dialysis access we had put in and said, "I won't be needing this."

If I had any doubt about the ability of people to program themselves through their beliefs to succeed or fail, this true story effectively erased that doubt. Again and again, we find that every disease or illness involves larger central issues in the individual's life, usually those issues are in their belief systems.

What about babies and children? As I said, the very young are very sensitive to the environment they are born into. They absorb the beliefs, fears and doubts. It is as if they telepathically learn the rules of the society they are born into and they will hang onto the beliefs even if it burns them.

Many people protest and are quite upset when it is suggested that they may be harboring negative beliefs which result in their illnesses. They cannot conceive that they could possibly have a hand in their own suffering. Mothers of young children are quite intolerant to this idea because they generally love their babies and children. Please note that the idea of uncovering harmful beliefs is not intended to lay the blame on anyone. The only thing useful about identifying negative beliefs is that we can then change them or replace them with positive ones.

What if they are not able to identify the negative beliefs causing the disease? We can still resolve the disease. Remember, I said that getting to the beliefs is the most direct route to changing the disease state. It is not the only way. We can work through the elements of the persona components to the next level, the realm of emotions.

Disease in the physical body is more often than not reflected back into our consciousness as a feeling. Be it depression, sadness, lack of energy or pain, disease is experienced as a degree of negative emotional energy. This phenomenon has captivated the interests of the medical profession all over the world since recorded time. Witch doctors with no knowledge of human anatomy or modern medical technology relied on manipulation of the emotions for diagnosis and healing of diseases. In western civilization, the old family doctor who had little or no access to medical technology relied on working with the emotional (energy) climate of the family for solutions in disease states. Even our current spiritual healing practices take place in the domain of emotion. Typically, the (vibratory) emotional energy level of the sick is worked up to a pitch that is incompatible with the continued existence of the disease. In religious practices, at this level, a belief in the healing power of a higher spirit is accepted by the individual as a replacement for their unconscious noxious negative beliefs.

Are these practices good? I don't know. Are they valid? Absolutely, they are all valid. They are just different paths to the same end and this is as it should be. Because, if there was only one path, there would only be one person, and there are millions of us humans in the world. All these paths recognize the importance of emotional energy and health and they are all valid.

Numerous studies have shown that a drop in the emotional energy level can predispose an individual to disease and may even shorten the person's life. There is evidence that men and women whose spouses have died live shorter life spans than those who have their spouses. It was also illustrated that when these bereaved spouses remarry or even acquire a pet to love, it has helped to prolong their lives.

Babies deprived of human love will fail to thrive and may even die. Studies have been done on small, isolated pockets of societies all over the world where there is a high level of integration among the members of the society. It was reported that the members of these societies typically touched and embraced each other a lot, showed a high level of unconditional acceptance towards each other, and expressed joy habitually. It was found that there were virtually no diseases or illnesses among these groups of people.

People's emotions can truly be said to have the power to kill them or to keep them alive. Emotional energy levels can, therefore, serve as a very good barometer of physical well-being.

In our metamedicine weight control program, virtually every aspect of the prescribed regimen is designed to elicit or support a higher emotional energy level of living. In fact, in the sessions following the first metamed session the participants are not asked how much weight they have lost or whether they are eating less food. I ask them to describe any changes they have noticed in their feelings towards their jobs, families and friends. They generally report that they have more energy for everything. Even the individuals who were not fond of their jobs found new interest in getting the jobs done in the most expeditious manner. They are alert and they radiate joy. And of course they are also losing weight and are feeling wonderful.

The emphasis on their attitude—their emotional energy climate—is based on the knowledge that a person's activity level depends on his/her energy level. Put in energy language, one will only experience the reality of one's vibratory frequency of energy which corresponds to their emotional level. Future medical technology can create miracles by tapping into this knowledge.

Once the participants in the metamed weight control program have achieved a higher emotional energy state, they are no longer who they used to be. They have changed themselves into individuals who can no longer have an overweight problem. Therefore, the weight loss is a matter of course. The eating programs prescribed are a ritual which supports their belief system.

Disease recognized at the emotional level is generally experienced as being "out of balance." Being in balance means that the individuals are on their true path of being the best possible human beings they can be in this life. It indicates that one is being one's true self. This is why, quite often, working in a field that excites us keeps us healthy and happy. Abnormal heart rhythms have been known to revert to normal when such patients take on a hobby they love or quit jobs they hated. The current concepts of the damaging effects of stress have their roots in this idea.

Recently, I was asked to see a cancer patient who suffered from intractable vomiting, as well as hypertension and dangerous abnormal heart rhythms. She was hooked up to the cardiac monitors in her hospital room. I was between surgeries and I had very little time to spend with her so I went straight for her emotional energy. I discovered that this patient was an artist once, a long time ago, and that she was very proud of that skill. I used this fact to balance her emotional energy level and as I watched the cardiac monitor, I saw her heart rate drop down to normal and all the abnormalities of rhythm vanish. I anchored this state and brought it to her attention. She stopped vomiting and was discharged from the hospital the next day.

By paying attention to your emotional energy level and keeping it in balance, you can guarantee yourself a life of health and joy. So how does one achieve emotional balance?

"I can't help the way I feel!" many people complain, and they are right. They won't be able to control their emotions until they take responsibility for them, until they acknowledge that each individual *chooses* to feel the way he/she feels. Once we take that step, we are on our way to choosing the emotions we prefer or to changing the emotions we do not want by using thought. Nobody else can make you feel any emotions you do not choose to feel or agree to feel.

Now, let's look again at emotional balance. When one reaches emotional balance, one is aligned with one's true self, which can be described as one's signature energy vibration. We get to emotional balance by doing what excites us at any and every given moment in time. Excitement or desire is the signal that lets us know that what we are doing is in line with what we need to be doing to be truly who we are. This is the meaning of the counsel, "follow your heart."

> *"Thought means life — Thinking makes the man."*
> *- A.B. Alcott*

Thought is the action that transcribes the disease in the personality into the physical disease we experience in the body. Thinking or mentality is the "doing" of the persona and disease is tantamount to abnormalities in thought.

We are familiar with psychiatric disorders as diseases of mentality—deranged thinking. Most of these mental disorders become noticeable or evident only because the rest of us, who consider ourselves normal, have the ability to stay within our society's agreed-on idea of what the world is. Those we call "deranged" lack

111

the strategy to do this, or if they have it, they are not applying it effectively. This is why NLP's techniques have become so tremendously successful in getting these patients back to "normal" behavior. And yet the medical profession is for the most part still ignorant of the fact that the science and methodology of neurolinguistic programming exists!

Of course, you don't have to be insane to appreciate the part thinking plays in health and disease. It is estimated that fully 80 percent of adult human diseases are the result of abuse of food, alcohol, drugs, tobacco, etc. In other words, these illnesses are diseases of human behavior which are actions of negative and erroneous thinking. All trauma, diseases of nutrition such as obesity and gastrointestinal diseases, most infectious diseases, many kinds of cancer, cardiovascular disorders and many others are directly related to negative thinking. The other 20 percent are the proceeds of non-optimum thought in more subtle manners. It cannot be otherwise for:

"As you think, so it is."
- Ancient wisdom

The actual course of an illness is, in large part, determined by the patient's thought. The patients who refuse any responsibility for their disease will avoid engaging the power of thought during their illnesses. These individuals become passive and dependent upon everyone around them. By refusing to think they in effect, abandon themselves to the ravages of the disease because they haven't taken any steps towards reconstructing the fundamental causative factor which is their negative belief system.

People who think in positive terms about their disease are taking the first valid steps to healing themselves. And this is the rejection of negativity. You can only build a positive belief systems with positive thoughts. In the rejection of negativity, they are on their way to changing the negative belief system, the causative factor in all disease. This is why these people achieve cures in illnesses that have been labeled incurable, such as certain cancers and even AIDS.

The pattern of thought, as well as the contents of thought, determine what effects the disease will have on the body during an illness. Two doctors suffered heart attacks. One is a surgeon in his mid 50's and the other is a cardiologist who has just turned forty-five. The surgeon whom I will call Sam Riley, got angry when he was told the course and prognosis of his disease.

"I know all that shit!" he yelled at Doctor Adams, Chief of the Cardiology Department of the hospital. Sam then spent his time terrifying the young Intensive Care nurses assigned to him with his angry demands. Finally, a tough older nurse, Ida, came forward and offered to take care of Sam. For the first few days, she watched Sam work himself up into fits of anger. At first, she would just offer him the antianginal drugs. Then, one time when he became angry and almost keeled over with pain, Ida just stood there and watched him.

"Goddamn it, don't just stand there," he gasped, reaching out with his right hand for the Nitroglycerine tablet.

"You can stop the pain yourself," Ida said flatly. "By now you should know that going against the grain gives you splinters."

Sam fell back against his pillow and allowed his tears to flow freely. "Nurse Ida was right," he thought. He thought about his life and the life of his patients. He concluded that all pain, physical and emotional pain comes from resistance. He saw that there cannot be pain without friction. He turned down a recommendation for cardiac bypass operation and asked to be discharged from the hospital.

"I want to spend some time getting to know my kids," he told Doctor Adams.

"You don't get to know your kids by dropping dead," Adams scolded. "Sam, don't be a stubborn fool!"

"Don't worry. I'll be around for a long time," Sam assured him.

Sam went home, closed down his practice and spent the next six months learning and achieving relaxation. He engaged in activities that held his interest and he found himself worrying less and was surprised to discover that life was really quite easy and that the world was beautiful. He became a happier man and began a new career in Sports Medicine.

The other cardiac victim, the cardiologist, Allen Jacobs, was just that—a victim. From the first day of his heart attack, he was paralyzed with fear. The laboratory studies, especially his cardiac enzyme studies governed the way he thought and felt about his illness. One day, a first year resident in medicine walked into his room and announced that Jacobs' enzyme levels were dropping down to normal. Jacobs brightened up and that morning, cleaned and dressed himself without any assistance from the nurses. His mood was sunny and he was beginning to have doubts about his diagnosis. He was on his way to find Doctor Adams and confront him for failing to make an adequate differential diagnosis about his condition on his admission to the hospital, when a laboratory technician approached him at the nurses' station.

"Doctor Jacobs, I have been asked to recheck your cardiac enzymes," the technician said, and quickly added, "I am really sorry, but I have to have more blood samples."

"Why?" Jacobs asked glaring at the young woman.

"Sir, the machine was not calibrated right. All the readings this morning were abnormally low," she told him.

Jacobs collapsed into a chair and had to be wheeled back into his room. He passively agreed to cardiac surgery and remained despondent postoperatively. He never went back to his cardiology practice since he viewed every normal activity, including intellectual exercise, as a danger to his cardiovascular system. So, he was content to collect on his disability insurance policy and be coddled at home. He has since checked in and out of the hospital for ailments ranging from a sneeze to hemorrhoids, the symptoms of which he amplified into life threatening proportions. The last time I saw him, I sensed that I was in the presence of advanced senility, and the man wasn't even 50 years old yet. The contrast between this image of Jacobs and the current vibrant youthful figure of Sam Riley is proof that thought patterns do create heaven or hell in our bodies.

The meaning we give an illness determines, to a large extent, what that illness is. In other words, the contents of our thoughts define the disease. Nowhere is this more conspicuous than in the variations of pain tolerance among individuals or even among cultural groups in a society.

My husband, Norman, and I worked once at the small hospital in my home town in West Africa. We were donating our services as a surgical team to everyone from my town and from the surrounding towns and villages. Since the hospital had no anesthesia machine we performed all surgery, both major and minor, under local anesthesia. It was an exciting time—doing so much with so little! We were amazed at how creative we could get when there was a need for our skills. My husband, an American-born surgeon, was astounded at the hardiness of my people.

Once following a particularly difficult hernia repair, Norman told the patient that he may have a fair amount of pain and painstakingly instructed him not to lift any heavy objects for some weeks. The patient thanked him and left. I will never forget the look of utter astonishment on Norman's face when he looked out the window and saw his freshly postoperative patient heave a hefty load of yams onto the top of his head and trot off to the market.

"I can't believe this!" Norman exclaimed, "These people are not human."

"What is the matter, Doctor?" my father who had assisted him in surgery asked.

My husband explained that the small amount of local anesthesia we used for the surgery had completely worn off before the patient was discharged and that he had expected the patient to be in so much pain when he stood up, that he would never consider lifting anything.

"Don't these people have pain, Papa?" he asked my father.

"Oh yes, they do," my father assured him. I laughed and explained to my father that in the United States, patients are encouraged to avoid pain postoperatively.

Our people have pain just like anyone else, I told Norman. It is just that the man doesn't think that it is something bad. He expects his wounds to let him know that something good—a healing—is taking place in his body and in a way, he looks on his pain with gratitude. You will never hear him complain about the pain because he sees the pain as his friend and therefore, the pain is not painful in the usual sense that we know it.

And it wasn't painful to the man because he did not perceive pain in that way, as something unpleasant or as something to avoid. He embraced the sensation we call pain as just that, a sensation. To him, the meaning of pain is the sensation that healing, a positive event is taking place. So he does not resist it or fight it. He integrates it within himself and flows with it. Therefore, he lives in peace and in relative comfort. This man's surgical wound healed without him ever taking as much as an aspirin for pain. In fact, it would never have occurred to him that there would be any necessity for him to take any medication for pain.

It is with our thoughts that we create the friction, the resistance to our natural selves which we experience as disease and pain. And if, as the refrain of the song says:

> "Now I haven't got time for the pain
> I haven't the need for the pain—"
> - A popular song

And if you have now decided to do something about it—to change it, read on.

7
Metamedicine: Methodology

The secret of the metamedicine practitioner's excellence is total focus on the patient. This integrated focus on the patient's well-being leaves no room for limitations, such as Prejudice, Avarice, Arrogance and Ignorance.

Flexibility in the choice of metamedicine tools as well as in the use of medical technology is a necessary skill for the doctor-healer. In other words, if a tool works, we use it. If it doesn't work, we choose something else until we find the tool which can get the job done.

Since metamedicine is modern medicine expanded to include the human consciousness factor, all the tools applicable in it are designed to enhance medical technology in producing powerful and quite often, spectacular results. Detailed description of modern medical therapy is beyond the scope of this work because this book is not intended to be a text on medicine.

The human brain is the personality's (persona's) fundamental tool for change, including healing. The idea we call mentality, which is the brain's thought component, is the specific agent for change in every aspect of the person.

I have stated that the first act of the doctor-healer is to gain entrance into the patient's world. The patient's world is his/her unique point of view. Stated simply, this means the way the person thinks or how a person internally represents experience.

Recall that in the chapter on "Thought," I delineated the universal language of eye movement patterns, "eye accessing cues," the verbs and the process (descriptive) words, which people use, are what reveal their thought processes. Remember also, that I stated the fact that by inducing people to be specific about their description of their experience, we can isolate the contents of the experience. In doing so, we prevent our natural inclination to interpret that experience. This way, we won't confuse our own interpretation of the event with what the people think the event is. Put to use, the knowledge of these parameters of the thought process will become the key to achieving rapport with any individual.

Why is it necessary to establish rapport with anyone? It is because people like and trust those who are like themselves. The one area where the mass-agreed on law of "Opposites Attract" does not work is in human relations. We tend not to open ourselves up to people who are unlike us. We unconsciously avoid them or shut them out of our privacy. And when we convince or rationalize ourselves into baring our souls to these noncompatible others, we find that we must struggle consciously to do so. It is not an easy procedure.

The explanation for this phenomenon relates to the fact that we human beings are energy forms. Recall that what differentiates energy or what makes various energy patterns different from each other is their amplitudes and vibratory frequencies. The unique vibratory pattern that distinguishes individuals can be regarded as their signature vibratory energy pattern. In humans, the emotionality aspect of the personality construct is the signature vibratory energy of the individual. As I described in the first section of this book, emotion (energy motion) comes before mentality in the hierarchy of persona construct and so quite often stays outside of conscious awareness. In other words, emotion is mostly an unconscious phenomenon.

Similar vibratory frequencies recognize each other. In other words, we can only function easily in the frequency with which we can identify. We cannot recognize or tune in to an energy unit of a vibratory frequency completely alien to us. This is why we unconsciously identify with people who are like us and quite often we are unable to say the reason why we prefer to deal with those individuals. The secret of rapport, intimacy or harmony is duplication or near replication of the (emotional) vibratory energy pattern of another individual.

To accomplish this we must mirror, match, and reflect back to an individual his/her view of the world. Therefore, we speak to the individual using the language gleaned from his/her eye patterns and process words. In addition, we mirror and subtly match the gross body physiologic actions such as breathing rate and body postures.

This latter maneuver can produce extraordinary results. At one of our training seminars, we had two individuals pair up. One of them, whom I'll label as person A, was instructed to relax and hold a thought, preferably a recall of a specific event. The other individual, person B, was positioned at a forty-five degree angle from person A. Person B was instructed to mimic A's breathing pattern and his limbs and posture were arranged in the same way A positioned hers. He was instructed to keep his eyes and facial expression the same as A's and to allow his thoughts to be whatever came to his mind. After a few minutes, the matching and mirroring was discontinued. Person B was asked to describe his internal perception. To person A's shock, he described exactly what A was thinking about! Now, does this bring "telepathy" to mind? Almost.

Matching and mirroring behavior must never be reduced to mimic. People's ego awareness or their conscious outer awareness have a built-in alarm which lets them know when someone is copying them movement for movement. It must be done with great respect and empathy for the individual being mirrored. In other words, you must show genuine or believable interest in the individual to produce the most effective results. We attain this by making use of cross-over mirroring. This is done by substituting one nonverbal channel for another. As an example, you can use hand movements to pace someone's breathing. You may also use the tempo of your voice to pace the person's breathing. Both will produce the same effects, although they may not be as powerful as mirroring breathing with breathing—that is, mirroring with the same system. Actually, cross-over mirroring is a bit safer maneuver to do. Can you imagine mirroring someone who is having an asthmatic attack? You may not live very long that way!

To test if you have done an adequate job of matching and mirroring both the verbal and non-verbal behavior, you attempt "leading" the individual being mirrored. Leading means generating behavior in the individual by offering them a behavior from yourself to match. For example, after matching and mirroring an individual for a while, change your posture and see if he/she follows suit. Once leading succeeds, you will have the following information:

a) You have succeeded in entering the other person's world.

b) You have the individual's unconsious trust because you have matched his/her (emotional) vibratory frequency.

c) The person is now ready to allow you to lead him/her to new behavior, decisions, and choices.

The metamedicine doctor, who is skilled in neurolinguistic programming or NLP, will normally accomplish all of this in the process of getting the medical history of an illness from the patient. There are some doctors who do this unconsciously without NLP training. These doctors rely on love—given unconditionally, to match identity with the patient and the patient instinctively trusts them completely .

Having paced, matched and led the patient successfully, the healer/doctor has now aligned himself or herself with the patient's viewpoint of the world. I will use the case history presented on the first chapter of this book to illustrate how the metamedicine doctor uses rapport to help a patient toward healing, since you are already familiar with that story.

Recall that Doctor Norman initially encouraged the patient,

Elmer Wenzel, to speak freely about his life on the farm in general. He was in no hurry to get to what Elmer was there for, which is his illness—a bleeding duodenal ulcer.

Doctor Norman considered the time that he spent listening to Elmer rattle on about his farm extremely valuable. It was at this point, when the patient felt safe and relaxed, talking about something other than his illness, that he yielded vital information about himself.

The doctor used the time to match, pace, and lead Elmer and achieved rapport quite easily. By the time he actually got into the history of Elmer's illness, he had an accurate knowledge of the way Elmer's brain processed information. In other words, he knew how Elmer thought.

Doctor Norman also discovered the activity that excited or interested Elmer the most. It was "piddling away the time" at the catfish pond, as Elmer put it. That was what he enjoyed the most. Why was this information so important?

First, Doctor Norman learned that this activity, that is, work related to the fish pond, would be what would align Elmer with his signature vibratory (emotional) energy. He would rely on this activity to kick up Elmer's emotional energy to a pitch which would either heal him or make it possible for Elmer to sense the cause of his illness—his disease.

Doctor Norman skillfully used Elmer's "operating language"– his representational system, which is mostly visual-kinesthetic, to get him to fully cooperate with the usual medical regimens relating to his particular type of illness. The doctor went through the usual medical diagnostic and therapeutic regimen. He would do this even if he was certain that Elmer could heal simply through a change in the underlying belief system, which is the causative factor in this disease. His decision to engage the usual medical course of therapy is strictly based on a deep respect for Elmer's belief in modern medicine. It was this belief that brought Elmer to the doctor's office to begin with.

Doctor Norman elegantly used Elmer's convincer strategy to

nudge him into choosing the work he loved. Recall that Elmer had bought into his parents' belief, which was that working a catfish pond was not a proper job for a man. As we saw, this belief was the cause of his disease. The doctor subtly went after this culprit belief by eliciting Elmer's decision-making strategy. He got this by asking Elmer how he decided to come to his office. Elmer had answered that having seen the third emesis and suffered through that bout, he told himself that he ought to go see Doctor Norman. His decision strategy here is visual-kinesthetic-auditory digital, or V-K-A^D. So, Doctor Norman presented Elmer with the most resourceful choice in this format: "And when you see how well it works for you, how good it makes you feel, you can tell yourself that you're doing the right thing."

It was like Elmer himself voicing his own decision because this is how Elmer makes decisions. So this choice clicked into place in Elmer's brain.

As Elmer began spending time at the catfish pond doing the work he loved, his emotional excitation raised his energy frequency to a level where he was no longer an energy being who contained the disease manifested as a duodenal ulcer. His rapid success at the catfish operation is evidence of his change of belief.

"Suppose Elmer longed to work the catfish pond but could not give up his belief, what then?" you may wonder.

If he desired to make this change and experienced difficulty doing so, Doctor Norman could have used NLP submodalities manipulations to change the belief elegantly. As it was, this was rendered unnecessary by Elmer's conscious choice of a new belief in doing the work he loved for a living.

Please note that throughout the event, Doctor Norman kept Elmer in a resourceful state because he appreciates the importance of positive emotional (energy) states in the healing process and in health. At their first encounter when Elmer demonstrated a surge of negative emotion, when he was overcome while talking about government impact on his farm, the doctor interrupted this pattern with a joke. Elmer laughed and that centered him. In other words, that returned him to his zero-rest balance point of energy state. Doctor Norman also anchored a set of positive emotions of laughter on his shoulder. He also future-paced him with those anchors to assure that thought of his cotton farm would no longer produce negative emotions for Elmer. Notice that the doctor tested this and confirmed that it worked before Elmer left the office.

All of Doctor Norman's metamedicine tools were directed towards kicking Elmer's emotional energy towards his true signature vibratory frequency and in that state, he was no longer a person who had ulcers. Furthermore, in that state, he became his true expression in life and so he became a productive, healthy and happy human being.

Often people who suffer from what is believed to be life threatening illnesses, become literally paralyzed by fear. We see this sometimes in women who have breast cancer. Some of these breast cancer sufferers are so frightened that they deny the existence of the disease, and mentally run away from it. I have actually had to physically run after a woman who suffered from breast cancer.

Her surgeon had gently explained to her that her breast biopsy was positive for carcinoma and mapped out a course of therapy. She placidly listened to the doctor and showed no emotion whatsoever. She agreed to the scheduled breast surgery. To all appearances, she was a brave and intelligent woman, but her doctor was not totally convinced of this. So he urged me to see her immediately. When I arrived at the examining room, I discovered that she was gone. I looked out the window and saw her walking down the street and I gave chase.

I ran after her and caught up with her. I introduced myself and she looked at me with glazed eyes and a frozen smile. I brought her back to the surgery center and I found it necessary to do a fear neutralizing procedure before she could communicate effectively. This procedure is covered in the section on "Mind Magic."

With the fear out of the way, we use rapport methodology to enter the patients' world in order to view their mental processes, their emotional climate and most importantly, their belief systems.

123

In the case of this patient who has been scheduled for breast surgery, she was able to recover a measure of emotional balance once she lost her fear. As if a veil was lifted off her eyes, the entire drama of her disease unfolded to her with crystal clarity. She told me that when she was twenty-two years old, her mother was discovered to have breast cancer. She began to entertain a fear that she too would develop breast cancer. Her fears escalated up to a point where a part of her knew that she would have breast cancer and that it would be just a matter of time. When the fear became uncontrollable, she simply put the thought out of her mind. She avoided regular breast examinations and mammography .

During the fear neutralization procedure, she had also vented her rage and now she spoke calmly and in a detached manner about her experience in living with fear. As you may recall, fear is the polar opposite of belief. It is belief in the negative. My task was to have her change this negative belief into a belief in something positive. Therefore, I had her construct a vision of herself that no longer contained breast cancer and I had her live in that self. She was future-paced to a period past her surgery and past full recovery. Her new image of herself became her new belief.

Before surgery, she was already looking forward to filling her household with music and laughter. She made a remarkably rapid recovery from surgery. In fact, her breast appeared more beautiful after the surgery than it ever was. She radiated health and we felt gratitude for sharing in her joy.

I have found that it is never too late to use the metamedicine approach to seemingly hopeless situations during illnesses. I was once asked to give an anesthetic to an extremely frail old woman who suffered from advanced cancer of the pancreas. This woman whom I will call Rose, was eighty-two years old and had lost a lot of weight. She was lying on a stretcher in the hallway of the hospital operating room when I first met her. She had curled up in the fetal position and was lying there facing the wall of the corridor. I was told by the nurses that she did not communicate verbally and that she had no idea of what was going on. I carefully lifted the cover off her face, leaned over toward her ear and announced, "I am the most beautiful thing you'll ever see and I am here to make you happier than you have ever been."

She slowly turned her head and looked at me. Then I told her who I was—her anesthesiologist. She began to turn away and I made a remark about the beauty in her eyes. She smiled shyly. After I established rapport with her, I asked her to tell me what she knew about her illness and the planned surgery. She allowed that she knew that she had lost a lot of weight and needed to be able to eat to gain weight. She denied any knowledge of her cancer. I sensed a rebellion and a certain defiance in her speech.

"You are a feisty little s.o.b. just like me, aren't you?" I teased her, slapping her gently on the shoulder. She burst out laughing. She propped herself up on her pillow and told me a couple of stories about her battles with disease.

"And I always lick 'em too," she concluded, relaxing back on her pillow.

"Then why not give'm hell this time too?" I asked. "You haven't forgotten how to fight. Have you?"

I saw her eyes brighten up and her breathing improve. I got her to talk about her happiest times and I anchored her most resourceful states. She understood that it was the body that healed itself. In rapid order, she told me that she had succumbed to frustrations and chronic unhappiness. She said that the worst thing she did to herself was allow fear and morbid thinking to become her daily diet.

"That nervousness has to go now because I ain't got time no more for that foolishness," she concluded.

By the time we got her on the operating room table, she was telling me about how she loved dressing up in pretty clothes and how she was always the best dancer in her neighborhood. I told her that I wanted to see her pretty dresses and that she would need to get out of the hospital as fast as possible to show me her clothes. I pressed her to tell me how soon she would get out of the hospital. After a pause, she told me that she would do it in seven days.

As we got her ready for anesthesia, she hid her face in her

hands and I thought at first that she was crying. Then I realized that she was giggling.

"What's so funny, Rose?" I asked, surprised. She said that she had forgotten that she wasn't wearing her false teeth and was embarrassed to be seen without them! We laughed and assured her that she looked pretty without them. She laughed until she was unconscious under general anesthesia.

Her pancreatic cancer was too advanced and only what is known as palliative procedures to bypass her obstructions were done. Nonetheless, she made a remarkable recovery from the surgery. Her surgeon had skill in metamedicine tools and used this skill to get her intestinal motility back within one day. Within forty-eight hours, she was eating food. In exactly seven days, she was discharged from the hospital.

I saw her during her post-operative visit at our center in the following week. She showed me her pretty dress which she said that she wore just for me. I asked her how she was doing at home. She said that she found herself getting upset with the people who were taking care of her at home.

"Then why don't you take care of yourself?" I asked her.

"I am still too weak," she explained.

"Baloney," I replied, "you have always been strong and you have enough strength to do whatever you truly want to do. Now, why don't you get off your behind, and take care of your family for a change?"

Later that evening, I saw her at the local grocery store, and I couldn't believe it was the same frail weak woman that I had talked with two hours previously. She moved with ease, wheeling a grocery cart from aisle to aisle, picking and choosing her food. She exchanged greetings brightly with other shoppers. I finally walked up to her to verify that what I was witnessing was indeed real. She gave me a hug and to the question in my eyes, she answered, "I knew I'd be alright. All I needed was to see you."

"Well, you don't need to see me for that. All you have to do is the remember always that you are the boss of this entire ninety pounds of lively flesh and bones," I told her.

Rose may eventually choose to translate out of this physical life using the cancer, but she will do so without fear. She will do so with full self-empowerment, holding her head high.

Metamedicine is the art and science of medicine practiced within the context of the total human conscious awareness, which we recognize as the personality or persona. In the section of this book called "Metaphysiology," we have seen how the human body is an integral part of this personality complex. The description of the body as the physical portion of the outer aware consciousness, or focus, is the same as saying that the body is the physical representation of the mind. The validity of this unity or integrated view remains intact, even as we make distinctions between the mind and the body for the purposes of description. Please recognize that we human beings have learned and functioned by making distinctions, separations and limitations or compartments in everything and in every idea since we started keeping linear time. Whether this is good or bad, I don't know. I do know that it does work for us to a degree. However, we have discovered that the integrated approach to human illness which is the metamedicine technique produces more powerful results.

Therefore, when presented with an ailment or illness, the doctor-healer focuses attention on the entire person beginning from obtaining a history of an illness to making the diagnosis and prescribing treatment. This is a far cry from what is generally taught in medical schools as a proper professional approach to diagnosis and treatment. We are taught to have the patient get to the point— to describe what it is that hurts, without digressing into talk not related to the actual organ or part containing the malfunction. The professional attitude encouraged in the future physician is that of distancing oneself from the patient's life. I remember being severely reprimanded as a third year medical student because I held a conversation with a psychiatry patient instead of remaining aloof and listening only. I didn't buy into this belief of non-communication even in those early years. I figured that the patient would be better off talking to a bartender. That patient would at least get a drink and feedback from another human being. As it was, he probably got crazier thinking that he was just talking to himself! One thing I do know by experience is that it is definitely more fun focusing attention on the personality rather than parts of the body. If you do that, you will be fascinated to discover that people are stranger than fiction and more powerful than any drugs invented by mankind.

To do an effective job of paying attention to the entire energy unit known as a person, a human being, the healer or doctor-healer needs to approach every such interaction with: integrity, curiosity, open-mindedness, and behavioral flexibility.

Let us take a look at each one of these attributes in order to appreciate their values.

Integrity

In metamedicine, integrity stands for being integrated. This means the recognition of the unity, soundness, and completeness of the basic unit of energy a person is. Remember that energy can neither be created nor destroyed. It can only be changed.

Those who practice with integrity recognize that they are as powerful as they need to be to get anything they want without hurting themselves or anybody else in order to do so. They also recognize that everyone else has this property. They respect this fact in other people whether these people are ignorant of their power and nature or not.

This is why the doctor practicing with the metamedicine methodology, has no need to play God. These doctors have no need to convince or force the patient and co-workers to think that they are powerful in order to make them feel powerful. This doctor will empathize with you because he/she can identify with the energy you are. Notice that I said empathy, not sympathy. The healer-doctor will discipline himself or herself and keep a respectable distance from sympathy because sympathy is in a sense, a show of disrespect.

How? Well, let us say that I choose to forget my integrity and begin sympathizing with poor Mrs. Jones who suffers these terrible pains. I am in effect saying, "Mrs. Jones, poor you. You are stuck." If Mrs. Jones knows better and respects her own power, she may resent it.

"Well, thanks a lot, asshole!" she may say. "Thanks for your faith and trust in my power to heal myself!"

Showing empathy is a more resourceful attitude. Empathy would motivate the healer-doctor to work to bring the patients up to speed in recognizing and believing in their personal power. The process of doing this can be quite simple and rapid. Here is a simple way I introduce patients to this idea.

"Mary," I would say, "Tell me this: does your body heal when you get a bruise or a cut?"

"Of course it does," she would answer.

"What do you suppose makes it heal?" I would ask.

"I don't know," she might answer, "It just heals, that's all." Or she may say, "I don't know. I guess God makes it heal."

"Do we both agree that the power of healing is in your body, no matter how it got there?" I asked.

"Yeah, that's true," she agrees.

"And it is your body. So that power belongs to you. Does it not?"

"Sure. I never thought about it that way, but you are right, Doctor."

At this point, I continue and tell her that all we do as doctors is create a condition that allows the body to heal itself. How fast and how well the body cures itself depends entirely on her. Her curiosity from this point on will determine how much of her own self-empowerment she learns to apply. At the very minimum, she begins to recognize her responsibility for her progress and her healing.

The quality of integrity is the motivating force behind the healer-doctor's drive to gain access to the patient's world through rapport.

Curiosity and Open-Mindedness

These qualities are a natural product of healing with integrity. When I look on the patient and know that this individual's *natural state* is health and joy, I immediately become curious to know why he/she would consciously or unconsciously choose otherwise.

So, while Joe Jones is telling me about his explosive headaches and inability to sleep, I am listening with more than my usual doctor's ears. I am listening with all my senses because I know that I won't limit my diagnostic work to the usual differential diagnoses of headaches and insomnia. I will have to look at the choices he is making with his illnesses fundamentally; what their purposes are and how they are serving him. To do this, I must gain access to Joe Jones' world—himself. I make liberal use of NLP methodology to achieve rapport with him which makes it easy for him to allow me into his reality.

To clearly see Joe Jones' world, I must be open-minded. This simply means that I would have to suspend my judgement on the person Joe Jones is and the circumstances of his life. Otherwise, I will not get a clear picture of Joe's life since I would be clouding it with my own bias of it—my own judgement. Please don't confuse this kind of open-mindedness with the traditional medical judgement. Medical judgement is an objective scientific way of evaluating observed data relating to an illness. On the other hand, open-mindedness in metamedicine says, in effect, that you hold the patient's view of his world—his reality—as valid. You will not invalidate it by judging it. Remember that this individual's viewpoint has served him, otherwise, he would not be alive. However, it may not have served him the way he would prefer. Whether it has been of service to him positively—the way he would prefer, or negatively—the painful way, it still serves him, nonetheless. My job is to assist this individual in making other choices that will return him to the natural state of health. To do an adequate job of this, I would need behavioral flexibility.

Behavioral Flexibility

Suspending personal judgement allows one to see things from many angles, or points of view, and to respond with a great deal of behavioral flexibility in achieving a desired outcome. In the case of Joe Jones, the outcome is to relieve him of the illness and assist him in returning to a natural state of health. I will keep changing what I do until we arrive at this outcome.

It is apparent that, in seeking conventional medical help by going to see a physician, Joe Jones' belief system contains a belief that medical science will relieve his condition. I respect this and I act accordingly. After an adequate work-up, which may include neurological and radiology studies, I will prescribe or recommend medical or surgical therapies in accordance with the diagnosis. Then, I will advise Joe that the treatments may relieve the pain, the illness, but may not cure the problem. And do you think Joe's interest will be ignited? You bet! Especially after I teach him to change state to feel any way he wants using Richard Bandler's NLP submodality techniques.

Joe Jones' curiosity will lead him to ponder the question of what the headache and its miserable effects are doing in his life.

"For one thing, you now know that you would rather not have headaches," I suggest.

"Silly statement," Joe states to himself, but he says to me, "Of course, I know I don't want that pain. I am not a masochist, you know."

"I didn't think you were," I say. "If you want to get a handle on this illness, the first thing you have to do is own it. By that, I mean that you consider it something that came from you."

"Hell, Doctor, I wouldn't give myself a headache. Why would I do something like that?"

"You wouldn't bump against the wall in the dark, but you do anyway," I counter.

"I see your point, Doctor," he says after reflecting a bit, "but,

131

I don't see why I put this headache in here," he said pointing to his temple.

"If you want to fix something," I say, "it is important that you own that thing first, because you cannot change what you don't own. It doesn't matter if it is something you like or hate; just accept it as yours. Only then will you possess it, and that gives you the power to deal with it as you please." Joe nods thoughtfully.

"So don't judge your headache and don't judge yourself as doing something wrong. There is no need for guilt in this. Just look at it and know that it is serving some kind of a purpose for you. Then, we will see if you can choose something else to provide you with the same service in a more pleasant way. Better still, you can choose to make this service unnecessary altogether and then you won't have to need the headache or any other substitutes. What will it be, Joe?"

"I would rather not have that type of service at all," Joe says emphatically.

"All right then, a little while ago, when you changed your state from boredom to excitement and joy, what did that do for your headache?" I asked.

"Oh, I didn't feel the headache at all," he answered.

"Good. Do you think that if you can keep up those feelings, that you may not have any headaches anymore?" I said and fired an anchor I had placed on his wrist.

"It is quite possible," he said beaming.

"What is the most exciting thing you do in the day? What are the things that you do that interest you the most?"

"Not much," Joe answers ruefully. "Besides, even if anything interests me, I'd be a failure at it. I am no good at anything."

"Anything?" I asked.

"Well, anything worthwhile," he explained .

"Of the things that are not worthwhile which you can do, which do you enjoy the most?" I asked.

"Oh, making models of cars, airplanes, trucks— anything that moves at all. I love designing them just as much as I love making them."

"Joe, who told you that these were not worthwhile things to do?" I asked curiously.

"I don't know," Joe said, "could have been my parents, I suppose." And Joe looked sad.

I take Joe through a belief change work. Then I take him through his Time Line where he makes changes in his past and future (See the chapter on Tools).

Weeks later, Joe returned to see me. He told me that his headaches were gone and that he was studying mechanical engineering and only working part-time on his old job to earn money for living expenses. He said he has never been so happy and thanked me for "saving his life."

"No, thank your headache for that," I said, amused.

"So, that's what that headache was all about," and a wave of revelation lights up Joe's eyes.

Notice that, in order to achieve the full outcome of healing the individual and relieving the illness, it was necessary for me, the healer-doctor, to blend and balance my skill and actions according to the needs of the patient's belief systems, emotions and thought processes. Had Joe not believed in taking medication for his headache after diagnosis showed no physiological findings as the cause of this illness, I would have taught him how to change the meaning of what he described as pain. That may give him just as much relief as any medication because to him that would be a believable tool for alleviating the pain.

A crucial step for the patient in the healing process is the acceptance of responsibility for the occurrence of the disease. This action is a declaration of personal empowerment—the patient begins to recognize that he/she is greater than the disease, the illness. The patient, having taken this action, can then begin to learn the lessons or the message which is the purpose of the disease to begin with.

It is important that the patient does not judge or invalidate the disease or condemn himself/herself for choosing the disease. No guilt is involved in this choice. This whole thing—the disease, the

133

illness—is just another valid tool we humans choose for learning. We may choose any illness as a mirror to reflect to us beliefs and choices we contain in order to decide whether they are what we want. If we don't prefer these choices or beliefs, we then proceed to replace them with better ones. That's all.

As soon as this is done, there will be no reason for the disease condition to continue. At this point, any tool we believe in the strongest—drugs, surgery or imagery will cure the illness.

Sometimes, the patient may be overwhelmed by the magnitude of the message of the disease and choose to translate out of physical existence in order to deal with it. Or, the patient may accept the healing and still decide to leave physical consciousness if he/she feels that the purposes for which they are physical have been served. Physical death is only a change in energy form. Remember that man, like all energy, cannot be destroyed. Man can only change states of conscious existence. A dying patient needs to have this knowledge. This is also a healing.

In addition to possessing a basic understanding of the human personality construct, human anatomy, physiology, and metamed disease processes, the metamedicine practitioner must avail himself/herself of a wide range of tools for achieving healing. Metamedicine tools encompass all the technology of modern medicine as well as other methodologies, such as neurolinguistic programming (including Time Line therapy), energy states imagery, hypnosis, meditation and relaxation procedures, and positive affirmations. Metamedicine tools are however not limited to those known today. Future metamedicine tools are as limitless as the human imagination.

8
Metamedicine: Tools

I magination is the dimension of the activity of the thought-mind. It is the unlimited space-screen wherein we think-create everything and every tool including disease, cures for the disease, health, prosperity and happiness.

Before I get on with the description of the various tools available in metamedicine, it would be useful to explore the subject of realities.

Realities

In the section of this work on "Thought," I stated that the brain does not differentiate between imagined and actual experience, when both are presented or perceived through the same sensory channels with equal intensity. Both experiences, the imagined and the actual, will produce an identical physiologic response in the same individual. Do the following exercise:

Pick up a fresh firm lemon. Feel the texture of its skin as you wrap your fingers around it and inspect it. Place it on a plate and cut it open. See the juice oozing out of it. Now, press it to your lips and lick the juice with your tongue. You feel your lips pucker as the tartness hits your taste buds.

Now, rinse your mouth out with clear water until you can no longer taste the lemon. Relax and close your eyes. Now, in your imagination, see a lemon, inspect it, cut it open and see the juice ooze out of it. Press it to your lips and taste the juice as you lick it. Notice that your lips pucker as you taste the tartness.

If you have done the exercise in your imagination with the same intensity of focus as the actual exercise, your lips will pucker just as they did when you actually tasted the lemon. Greater precision in the above exercise using imagination can be achieved using submodality comparisons (more on submodalities later). Now which experience is real? Both of them as far as our physiological body is concerned are real. Both the actual as well as the imagined, stimulated the same response from the body. Therefore, both events are real. The only differentiation to be made for the sake of reference is this: the actual event or experience is called physical reality and the imagined event is nonphysical reality. Take the next small step and recognize that all realities are equally valid.

Not only are physical and non-physical reality equally valid, they can be stored and used in any sequence and at any time that the conscious or unconscious mind chooses to use them. Experiences in these realities will produce physiologic effects on the physical body. Spooky? Not really. If you understand that the body is more or less the same unit as the brain, functioning as the brain's sensory channels and support mechanism, this will not surprise you. When you allow yourself to know this, you will understand that the physical body is *contained* within the mind, the electromagnetic energy field of your human consciousness.

This is why metamedicine is *not* a mind over body technology. Metamedicine recognizes that the mind and the body are the same complex, the body being contained within the (mind) consciousness. This order, this fundamental pattern of arrangements, is the key to the mystery of the so-called miraculous healings resulting from metamedicine techniques.

I have said that the tools applicable in metamedicine include the predominantly physical tools of modern medical technology as well as the other tools or methodologies that rely mostly on the direct action of mentality. These latter tools, which I will call

Mental Technology (MT), rely for their effectiveness on the fact that all realities are valid. Resources contained or exhibited in one reality can be transferred to another reality. The NLP Allergy Cure Model is an example of this. The patient in the dissociated state (nonphysical reality state) contains other resources lacking in the physical patient (physical reality). These resources are the physiologic components of a normally functioning immune system. The allergy sufferer has a defective immune system. We will not discuss the details of the components of the physiologic barriers involved in the immune response here. Nonetheless, the patient in the dissociated state does not have the allergic reaction the physical patient suffers.

A leading NLP practitioner tells the story of a psychiatrist who suffered from severe allergic reactions to onions. In the dissociated state under hypnosis, the practitioner had this individual eat an onion. He had no reaction whatsoever. This individual's wife witnessed the event. Afterwards, the doctor was told that under hypnosis, he had exhibited no allergy at all to the onion and the doctor's wife confirmed this. The doctor became enraged. He could not tolerate anything that his mentality judged as being counter to established medical beliefs.

The physical patient will need the resources contained in the dissociated state in order not to have the specific allergic reactions. In the Allergy Cure Model, the physical patient acquires the resources of his (nonphysical) dissociated self and this brings about a cure of the allergy.

Is this real? You bet it is. To date, the NLP Allergy Cure has 80 percent or better cure rate of diagnosed allergy cases. The usual medical desensitization regimen does not come close to this success record. For those who consider this a spooky practice and want nothing to do with it unless they can understand the process in conventional medical terminology, I assure you that the phenomena can be described as a type of desensitization. However, cross desensitizing in two states (two realities) is vastly more powerful than desensitization in a single physical state.

The metamedicine approach uses as many avenues as possible to arrive at a given destination, the cure. Therefore, it has a much better chance of arriving there.

Dissociation - Association

An adjunct to the idea of the validity of different realities is the ability of human beings to view themselves from different perspectives. This is known as dissociation. We dissociate ourselves from an experience or an event by viewing ourselves in that experience or event from another perspective.

Recall an embarrassing event. Relive it. Notice that you recaptured all the bad feelings. An example can be a wild party you attended with your best friends. Watch it as if you are watching a movie of the event. In the critical scene of the movie, you watch yourself making a fool of yourself. You find now that you may not feel as much embarrassment anymore about this scene. You are dissociated from the experience, that is, you are not physically in this experience. You are only viewing it from the sidelines.

Let us take this a step further, or rather, a step removed. Now, imagine watching yourself from another place, say the ceiling of the room, watching yourself view the same movie.

Did you notice that you now feel completely detached from the whole experience? You can, from this perspective, watch yourself making a fool of yourself at the party without feeling embarrassed about it. You know it is you doing these silly things, but it doesn't affect you. It is as if the whole event is happening to another person altogether.

We can therefore dissociate ourselves from our actions or experiences in order to view them objectively. In other words, we remove ourselves from the reality of the event or experience so we can evaluate or deal with it from a vantage point (of view). This is a useful skill to have because it makes it less likely or even impossible for us to indulge in the judgements and the resulting invalidations that prevent us from dealing with the experience in a more positive and more empowering manner. Dissociation from an unpleasant experience will permit one to view the experience objectively in order to extract the learning that permits one to grow from that experience, without lugging around all of the emotional baggage usually associated with it.

As an example, individuals who have experienced an unhappy relationship, such as a rough marriage, come out of the union with negative feelings of bitterness, anger, remorse and guilt. These negative emotions, which are quite often beyond their rational control, would prevent them from recognizing the positive opportunities inherent in such an experience. If you dissociate from the experience or memory of this event, you will be able to examine the whole relationship without the disabling negative emotions. While viewing it from this neutral ground, you may begin to become curious about why you attracted such a relationship in the first place. You can then learn something about how you think about yourself or what negative beliefs you hold about yourself. Having identified these beliefs, you can change them into positive ones and begin to treat yourself better. The result is that you can attract more satisfying relationships next time around. Had you continued to remain in the feelings of the negative memory, you would not be able to recognize this opportunity for personal change and you might go from one unpleasant relationship to another in a never ending cycle.

I make frequent use of dissociation to control pain for the patients at our ambulatory surgery center. For virtually every surgical procedure, it is usually necessary to puncture the skin and various tissues with a hypodermic needle for the injection of drugs or for insertion of an intravenous catheter which is used for infusion of intravenous fluids and medication during surgery. Quite often, I run into individuals who have a morbid fear of "needles." They come in all ages, sizes and shapes. I have seen a powerfully-built, "macho" male faint at the sight of a needle aimed at his forearm. I have also seen a delicate three year old girl watch an intravenous line being placed in her forearm without flinching. For those individuals who cannot tolerate "needles," I apply dissociation.

I normally begin by teaching them to relax. Then I ask them to imagine themselves watching the procedure from the operating room ceiling where they are nice and safe. From there, they can watch what is going on. I will test, using submodalities of their predominant sensory channels, to confirm that they have carried out this instruction. After this the patient is usually able to tolerate the venopuncture or percutaneous injection procedure with minimum fear and discomfort.

Quite often, since I believe that life is fun, I'll have the patient amuse themselves while in the dissociated state. I remember one grandmother, Mrs. Wells, who was scheduled to have eye surgery for the removal of a cataract and implantation of an artificial lense at our surgery center. Most eye surgeries there are done under nerve blocks using local anesthetic agents. The crucial block done for this particular operation is what is called the retrobulbar block. A long needle is passed into the back of the cavity containing the eyeball from the front of the lower eyelid and the anesthetic solution is deposited there to anesthetize the eye. Since nobody in their right mind would hold still if they saw a long needle heading towards their eyeball, we generally put these people to sleep very briefly in order to do the nerve block.

I couldn't give Mrs. Wells any drugs to sedate her, let alone put her to sleep with some potent drugs, because she suffered from severe kidney failure as well as other dangerous medical conditions. Her systems would not be able to metabolize the medications adequately, so it was not safe to give her intravenous drugs. We didn't cancel the surgery because she wanted it badly and pleaded with us to let her have "new eyes." She was bedridden and one of the few remaining pleasures she had was watching television. As her cataracts got denser and her vision increasingly more blurry, she was not able to watch television any longer and was quite upset about it. So I had to do something.

While getting into her world using rapport methodology, I discovered that the memories that gave her the most positive emotional state were those times she spent with her granddaughter. I anchored this state at its peak (more on anchors later). Then I had her as usual watch the procedure from a dissociated state, but this time I had her recall the most enjoyable time she had spent with her granddaughter. I instructed her to step into it and relive it, and as she became fully associated with it, I fired the anchor.

The nurses talked later about how weird it was to watch this woman smiling as the retrobulbar needle arrived at her eyeball. Not only that, she kept her eye open upon request for the injection. She looked so happy that I thought it best to let her enjoy herself throughout the surgical procedure.

Later, during her postoperative visit, I asked what she remembered of the eye surgery. She didn't remember much of it. She said," You know, Doctor, my family got worried about me."

"Why? " I asked her.

"Well, they said that for two days after the operation, I acted real weird. They said I laughed at everything anybody did. They must have thought I was drinking something. "

Then I remembered that I had forgotten to collapse the anchors and get her back to her regular reality, but I didn't bother to explain this to her. I merely answered that it was okay for her to have fun.

Dissociation is a very important tool used in NLP models for change work. The first time I saw the power of this tool at work was during a phobia cure of heights using the NLP model. The procedure took only five minutes and this individual was cured of his phobia of heights. He went up and down in the elevator successfully several times to demonstrate his cure. After that, I took a few minutes to cure myself of my life-long phobia of snakes using the same model. Up until that time, I avoided pet shops and the reptile section of every zoo because the thought of seeing a snake paralyzed me with fear. I used the NLP model to rid myself of this morbid, unreasonable fear. After the cure, I went into a pet shop, and for the first time in my adult life, I looked at a snake. I was amazed at what beautiful creatures snakes were! I am dumbfounded to discover that conventional psychiatry still insists on relying on long, costly and ineffective analysis for phobia control when NLP methodology has proven to be vastly superior in achieving permanent cure. The enormous power of dissociation was graphically demonstrated to me when I and several others used it to walk barefoot over a forty foot bed of red hot coals without incurring any trace of a burn.

The therapeutic power of disassociation in NLP methodology for change work would be incomplete without the use of association. Association, such as being associated in a past memory means that one is seeing through one's own eyes, hearing what one heard and feeling the feelings one felt then, as if the events stored in the memory are happening once more. In other words, the person is reliving the events of the memory. The disassociated state provides a means for viewing a past or future experience in an objective way in order to perceive the learnings and other resources it may contain. To actually go beyond cognitive perception of these resources and integrate them physically for the improvement of the life of the individual, it becomes necessary to fully associate and anchor the individual in the new state that now contains the new resources.

Anchoring as it is used in NLP is the purposeful application of a specific stimulus to produce a specific response each time the stimulus is applied. As an example: you are out on a date with someone you love. It is a romantic evening and you share a love song which produces a deep, warm feeling in both of you. Every time you hear that song on the radio, you get those warm feelings back. That song is then the anchor for that pleasant memory.

An anchor is a sensory stimulus paired with a specific response(s) or state(s). The sensory stimulus can he either internal as a feeling or a remembered picture or external, such as a touch or hearing a sound. Anchors explain most of our automatic behaviors. People who eat their lunch at noon will automatically get hungry when they look at their watches and see that it is noontime. Church goers get reverent when they hear church bells ring. The touch on the hand by someone, especially when you are in distress, gives you a feeling of comfort or closeness. A large section of the American economy known as advertising is based on anchors. The sight of a yellow arch will quite often compel children and adults alike to pull into a McDonald's restaurant for a hamburger even though they are not particularly hungry.

Why do anchors work? The human brain learns at lightening speed by association. Once a given stimulus, such as a certain touch on a specific part of the body triggers a certain response such as a smile; every such stimulus will produce the same type of response. In other words, every time you are touched that way at the same spot on your body you will feel a smile without thinking about it. The effectiveness of an anchor in triggering a given response depends upon the intensity of the state in which the original stimulus-response took place. Thus, when we make therapeutic use of anchors, it becomes important that the individual be fully associated in the state which we wish to anchor. For example, if I want to feel joy, I will search my memory for the times when I have felt most joyful. I will isolate the specific thing or person in those experiences that elicited the greatest feeling of joy in me. In this case, let us say that it is a child. I will think about this child and intensify my feelings of joy. When this feeling reaches its peak, I'll touch my left temple. Each time I touch my left temple at the same exact spot and in the same way, I will have a feeling of joy.

Are you beginning to see the value of anchoring as a tool for commanding a set of very positive feelings for yourself, if not for others?

"Oh, but that is manipulation!" some people cry about anchoring.

"Yes it is," I agree, "but look at what wonders it can create. Imagine what it can do for you in personal relationships."

What if you don't want an anchor anymore? No problem. You can simply create as many other different responses to the same stimulus as possible and confuse the hell out of your brain that way. Or, you can anchor the response on another part of your body and do the NLP maneuver called "collapsing anchors." Since this is not a book about NLP, I will not go into the details of that here.

With a little imagination, you can see how useful collapsing anchors can be as a method for ridding yourself of habitual responses or even pain.

Submodalities

One of the most powerful tools for changing human experience and behavior is Richard Bandler's NLP Submodalities patterns. Recall that in the section of this work on "Thought," I described the idea of the "Representational Systems." These can also be called "modalities." I had said that the way we think about any experience is by using sensory system representations. These are visual pictures, auditory sounds and kinesthetic feelings. Submodalities are the specific finer qualities or distinctions within each modality. The following are some of the submodalities in each of the three major modality or representational systems:

1. Visual
Brightness, Location in Space, Color/Black and White, Moving/Still, Size, Shape, Distance, Bordered/Panoramic, Dissociated/Associated, 3-D/Flat and Foreground/Background contrast.

2. Auditory

Loudness - Intensity, Pitch, Rhythm, Location in Space, Number of Sources, Music/Noise/Voice and Stereo/Monoaural.

3. Kinesthetic

Pressure, Area/Extent, Intensity, Temperature, Moisture, Texture, Duration, Still/Moving, Rhythm and Smell/Taste.

Submodalities of each modality are the way the brain codes, sorts, and stores experience. The many varieties of submodalities within each modality allow for more powerful patterns and faster ways of changing the programming in our human software of the brain. Thus, we can create personal change or the way we think about experience and the way we respond to it much more rapidly and with greater ease.

Here are simple examples of the effect of submodalities on experience:

Think about an experience that you enjoyed in the past. Close your eyes and bring up the memory of this experience. See what you saw at that time. Brighten the image and if it has colors, make the colors brighter and brighter. Stop. Now dim the image. If you are like most people, increasing the brightness intensified your feelings of enjoyment for the experience. Decreasing it decreased your feelings. By the way, this is a way to add more pizzazz to your positive experiences when you wish to relive them.

Now, I want you to recall an unpleasant memory where you couldn't get something someone had said to you off your mind. It could be your boss or your spouse making a negative comment about your abilities in a loud, high-pitched tone of voice. You kept hearing that comment over and over again in your head, so much so that you couldn't fall asleep at night. Now listen to that comment again. Turn down the volume of the sound and lower the pitch. Now how do you feel about if? You may find that the negative feelings you had about it decreased considerably. So now you know what to do next time you want to get a voice out of your head.

To date, the most awe-inspiring use of submodalities is changing belief. Up until Richard Bandler created the pattern for belief change, it was generally held that deeply held beliefs were extremely difficult if not outright impossible to change. Many believed that it required a mystical experience or severe trauma for one to change these core beliefs. Not so. Belief change is accomplished with relative ease and quite rapidly using Bandler's submodalities model for changing beliefs. When you recall that our life's experiences are products of our beliefs, you will begin to appreciate the depth of gratitude mankind owes to Richard Bandler's genius.

Most change work using submodalities is done by comparing the submodalities of the state or behavior we want to change to those of the desired ones. The submodalities making the greatest impact are then used to create the change. Again, because this is not a book about neurolinguistic programming, I will not describe the details of the submodality change patterns or models. The interested reader is referred to the many excellent NLP books on this subject. The following are some of the tools for personality change created from submodalities:

Changing The Present State

With the technical know-how of Bandler's submodality patterns, you can literally turn your life into pure magic. Just think, you never have to be bored again. You can intensify any resource state and you can have fun anytime, any place.

The value of this tool in metamedicine cannot be overestimated. Recall the importance of one's emotional (energy) state. When you lapse into a negative state (emotion), which is the usual case in disease states, kicking your emotional energy state into the positive realms changes the entire equation (situation) literally and instantly. In the positive states of energy, you make more resources available to yourself: for instance, your immune system begins to function better; you begin to recognize negative beliefs that your disease is pointing out to you. Now you are in a superior position to heal yourself. This is a required tool which every practitioner of metamedicine and indeed everyone must have in their "healing tool box."

Making Things Better Than They Should Have Been

In the same way we can change our present state, we can learn to make any experience–past, present and future definitely more exciting and more enjoyable. When the things we are doing are "sort of okay," and we are "just making the best of things" in the activities or events of our lives, it becomes obvious that we are operating from a negative emotional energy state.

We can elicit the strategy (the sequence of the submodality of the representational systems) of making things better than they should or can be and more exciting and more fun. In using this strategy, we "pump up" our feelings–energy state, which results in us acting in a different way then we normally would. Our approach to things using this new attitude is what creates a more exciting event or experience. This same pattern can be applied to a past experience we think and feel was disappointing or ho-hum. Disappointment requires planning. Think of it for a moment. In order to be disappointed, you would have had in mind an expectation, a certain notion of what the impending experience or event was to be. Otherwise you wouldn't have been able to experience the let-down feeling after the event takes place because you wouldn't have a standard against which to compare it. As long as you are going to have expectations, why not extract the strategy that makes them so tantalizing and use it to make the actual experience a real blast?

Eliciting A Motivation Strategy - Going For It

In the same way we discover the strategy of approaching events and experiences to make them more positive, we can examine the strategy structure of how to successfully motivate the self to do something. Essentially, we find out what individuals do inside their heads when getting motivated. We take note of their submodality sequence strategy and this can be applied to any other situations where they need to become motivated; for example, exercising regularly.

The corollary to this is that you can also use the same process to unmotivate yourself from doing things that you do not want to do but which you are likely to do, like overeating. The technique makes the event less appealing to you and is an excellent way of getting rid of bad habits.

Confusion To Understanding

Often, when most people are confused about something which they want to understand, but don't, they go about reaching understanding by getting more information. Two people may have the same amount of information on a given subject. One will understand the subject and another may be completely confused about it. Why does the one individual understand it and the other remain confused? "Well, obviously the fellow who understands it is smarter," is the usual answer. Not exactly. What the fellow who understands the subject has is the strategy—a sequential method of organizing the subject matter that makes for understanding it. So what do we do to get the confused fellow to understand the same subject?

We can study the structure of something he understands and elicit the strategy, the steps, or the sequence of submodality representations he used to reach that understanding. We can then apply this strategy to the confusion state. This individual would then go from confusion to understanding of the subject using the pathway that he normally uses to achieve understanding.

Another thing we can do is to elicit the strategy of the fellow who understood the subject. We have to make sure that his strategy is efficient and effective. In other words we want to be certain that he learns quickly and easily. We can then have the fellow who is confused use this strategy. When he does so, his confusion will give way to understanding.

In this second maneuver, what we are doing is using another person's process to learn. That we are able to do this means that understanding ideas can be a repeatable and predictable process. Does this make you wonder about the content of the thoughts? The fact that we are capable of understanding with the same amount of information what we were previously confused about tells us that most people have all the information they need to understand a thing. What we are lacking is an effective process of organizing this information. That is what effective learning is all about.

Where does this kind of learning fit in when it comes to health and disease? Can you use another person's learning strategy to know how to stay healthy and even how to heal your disease? Absolutely. If you know *how* someone stays healthy or makes himself pain free, you can do the same. This process of using another person's strategy is called "modeling."

In our metamedicine research, we seek out individuals who show certain outstanding capabilities for staying young, healthy, pain free, etc. We want to find out what they do and their strategy for doing these things effectively. We can then install these strategies in other people who lack the qualities necessary for staying young, healthy or painfree.

The most important application of using other people's processes will be in the area of achieving superior health. By now you are getting the impression that disease is a reflection of limitations, all self-imposed, in the personality or persona. That's right; disease is a symptom of a limitation. To truly get rid of a disease, you must get rid of the limitation. Can you imagine what you would be, what life would be if you no longer functioned with limitations? You would be a creative genius and you could create heaven on this earth for yourself and for others. Far fetched? Maybe but nevertheless, it is an achievable goal.

The Phobia and Post-Traumatic Stress Syndrome Cure

Under Dissociation-Association, I discussed the rapid phobia cure. A similar pattern can be applied to get permanent relief in post-trauma stress syndrome where individuals have been subjected to a horror so great that they blank out most of the details of the experience. They will then demonstrate an exaggerated negative response to a cue from the experience or similar experience, much like phobics do. Their behavior to them and to others appears unreasonable.

This therapeutic pattern or a modification of it may be useful in cases of victims of abuse, such as people who were abused as children or rape victims.

The Swish Pattern

People quite often have feelings that limit or inhibit their behavior in a negative way. An example would be a person who feels so out of control when they see chocolate that they are compelled to eat more chocolate than they should, or even want to. Submodalities that diminish the feelings that limit the individual's behavior are identified as well as those associated with a more resourceful state in the individual. The swish pattern is a format that uses the problem situation as the cue for change into a more resourceful state, by moving from the associated to the dissociated state.

This is a great tool for the elimination of undesirable habits such as smoking, nail biting, overeating and other problem behaviors. And, the success of the change work can be tested on the spot!

Eliminating Compulsions

Addictions and other compulsions which do not respond to other methods of change or patterns can be eliminated using what is known as "compulsion blow-out." In effect, the submodalities with the greatest effects are identified and in a 'blow-out' maneuver, the brain is overwhelmed using this. It is very dramatic and very powerful. I used this on a patient who was compelled to eat chocolate cookies. Afterwards, she baked chocolate cookies all day and had no desire to consume them. She told me that she could have eaten one if she had wanted to but didn't want to. This is important because all a compulsion blow-out is designed to do is to give individuals choice. They can choose to behave a certain way as opposed to being compelled to act in the same way. The important element here is control.

Attaining Kinesthetic States

Has it ever occurred to you that if you can recreate the feelings (both physical and the emotional) you got from taking any drug, that you would not actually have to take the drug anymore to obtain the effects you take them for? Yes, this is a reality. It is made possible with the application of patterns from the submodality sequences of the body sensations experienced while taking the specific drug. It can be said that the body is taught to relive the kinesthetic memory of the effects of the drug.

This is a method of experiencing the effects of a drug without actually taking it. The implication is that one can enjoy the benefits of the drug without the adverse side-effects one can have from actually taking the drug. The method used is simply to re-create the various sensations experienced after taking the drug in the same order that they are felt when the drug is actually taken.

If government resources were channelled into developing this tool for treating drug addiction, the war on drugs could shortly be over.

The ability of humans to recreate a kinesthetic experience, that is, a physiological response, which is an identical response to that induced by a chemical substance explains the placebo effect and gives us an insight into the function of drugs in the disease process. It has been recognized that placebos (inert medication) have the

151

same success as the actual medication in alleviating targeted ailments in a certain percentage of people. The effectiveness of placebos can be directly traced to the human brain's propensity to recognize and respond to cues. The brain simply triggers the same response to the respective body parts in response to similar cues, be it an active chemical agent (drug) or an inert one (placebo). It appears then that a medication, a drug, is more or less an anchor. Recall that an anchor is a specific stimulus which produces a specific response when it is applied. This makes one wonder what the real intention of drugs are and what their place is in the disease state. The fact that a drug's physiological effect on the body can be duplicated without taking the drug is an indication that the original purpose of the drug is to produce a physiologic-kinesthetic effect in the body which can be recorded in the brain and replicated. Replication? Therein is the rub. To successfully recall the physiologic effects of a drug requires learning and skill such as the NLP techniques of submodality utilization.

Drug dependency, or addiction, such as alcoholism and drug abuse, and even food abuse, are essentially illnesses of abnormal and compulsive use of anchors. In alcoholism, the alcohol is the anchor. It is the cue for a set of negative behaviors which represent a set of limitations. I have seen some food addicts who can only function by having food in close proximity. The strange thing is that these individuals may not actually ever eat the food! Food is only an anchor for accessing good feelings.

Please note that without the patient's belief that a chemical substance, be it an active or inert agent, can produce a desired effect, no drug in the world would be able to help a patient. The very action of taking a medication indicates that the individual's belief system contains a belief that says that the medication will produce the desired effect. This decision is usually made unconsciously.

Recruiting Unconscious Mechanisms

In metamedicine, we perceive disease as a tool. Disease is

usually judged as a negative tool used to bring to the attention of the conscious awareness some negative choices or limitations contained in the individual's belief system. The intention of any tool is for the provision of a service. The result of that service may or may not be what we desire. In the case of a disease which is a negative tool, the service is an illness which we experience as undesirable or negative events in the body. A distinction must be made here between the *intention* and the actual *event*.

In metamedicine, we make a bold claim that the intention is positive and here's why. The fact that we humans have survived as physical beings attest to our penchant for self-preservation. To put it simply, consciously or unconsciously, we love ourselves. We, therefore, presuppose a positive intention in every disease state. Our task in metamedicine is to find out where possible what the positive intention is. Most of the time this intention is to alert us about a negative belief or choice which we contain and which is blocking our progress to positive experiences in life. Some of the time the intention is to be of positive service to other humans. All in all, the intention is generally positive.

So, in metamedicine we view disease as a tool for a positive outcome, for making a positive change. An illness, the specific negative effect produced by the disease and which, in practical terms, we equate with the disease is what we experience in conscious awareness. When we place no judgement on the disease, we can begin to allow ourselves to discover the intention consciously or unconsciously. Once the intention of the disease is served, there will be no reason for it to continue to exist.

"Are you saying that all illness is then psychosomatic?" many people ask. Not really, what we are saying is that an illness occurs in a person whose body is contained in his/her consciousness. What we usually call a psychosomatic disease is an illness which we are unable to explain grossly or microscopically in the body. That we are unable to see it does not deny its existence. It is, nonetheless, experienced by the patient and so it is real to this individual.

Quite often, the patient suffering from the so-called psychoso-

153

matic illness is judged to be "wacko," who is out of touch with reality. "Whose reality?" we forget to ask. Remember that everyone has their own point of view. We are able to share aspects of our points of view with everyone else as a common reality. Nonetheless, outer aware consciousness including the body is each individual's unique point of view, each individual's private reality. Therefore, the idea of psychosomatic illness, the way we have used it in modern medicine up until now, is a moot point.

All illness, whether it lends itself to the recognition of medical science or not, deserves the attention of the healer because the patient must not be denied the opportunity to profit from the positive intention of the disease. One of the important benefits to the patient is learning to substitute a positive tool in the place of a disease (negative tool) as a means to obtaining the positive intention. This can be done consciously or unconsciously.

I have discussed some of the conscious processes of doing this. Locating and achieving a positive intent can be done unconsciously using hypnosis. It is a powerful tool which is not acceptable to many in the modern medical world, largely because of its lack of uniform standard and precision. Also hypnosis is not attractive to a lot of people who fear loss of control over themselves.

NLP's Reframing, especially the Six-Step Reframe, circumvents these objections to hypnosis while producing an equally powerful result. It contains elements of the trance states of hypnosis, but the individual, that is, the patient communicates with his/her unconscious mind and at the same time is able to communicate in conscious awareness with the healer or the therapist.

This is one tool where the spectacular power and creativity of the human unconscious mind can be appreciated. Using the power of suggestion, the patient can create thousands of parts in the unconscious realm to provide him with any benefits he/she desires. In the case of disease, the patient can create parts or choices in the unconscious that would replace disease in satisfying these positive intentions.

Once you go through this six-step reframing to rid yourself of a physiological ailment, there will remain no doubt in your mind that disease *does have* a positive intention. It works! This NLP tool is magnificent because the necessary positive changes are made without the usual conscious sense of struggle. I recommend that the six-step reframe be employed in most illnesses. This will at least take care of any residual intents of the illness which may have been overlooked. Like all powerful tools, caution is advised in its use. You must first acquire the skill through proper and competent training. Just as you don't perform major surgery by reading a book on surgery, you do not do the six-step reframe and some other powerful NLP patterns by reading a book about them. Training obtained from experts in this field is essential. This is why I have not gone into detail on these techniques.

Time Line Manipulation

From Neurolinguistic Programming, we learned how we process and utilize the information that comes from the world around us, that is, our outer aware consciousness. Patterns or models were developed from this body of knowledge and used for intervention (therapy) wherever necessary in bringing about changes in the personality. A direct development stemming from the curiosity in how humans process information is interest in how humans store information, or the idea of how we store memory.

We think and speak of experience in a linear sequence. We say, "Something happened yesterday; something is happening now, and something will happen tomorrow." Each person has an idea of the past, the present and the future. When you think of the past, where do you sense it? Some people will point behind themselves, others will point forward to their right side or their left side, etc. All in all, people will usually have a direction from which they sense the concept of the past. The same goes for the present and the future. If these directions of sensing the past, present and future memories or events are linked together, a line will usually result. It can be a line running from the front to the back of the person, or from side to side, or even a line that forms an arc or a circle. The common element is that the memories are arranged in sequential order.

Now we can actually at will go into our imagination and draw or visualize such a line called a Time Line. We can sense our experiences or memories arranged on it sequentially. Still within the screen of the imagination, you can rearrange these memories in a way you desire and in a way that removes limitations.

This is an extremely powerful tool. You can delete, replace, and arrange past memories. You can also create memories in the present and install it in the past and/or the future. You can change your feelings about these memories and install the new feelings in your entire Time Line wherever these memories occur. Incredible, isn't it? The ability to manipulate time pokes holes in our certainty about the solidity of our present physical reality. Are we going insane? No. We are just beginning to understand what we are. The demonstration that changes in one's past and future memory can be made from the present, lends validity to one of metamedicine's most powerful fundamental tools–living in the present. Read on.

9

The Treasure and the Cure

Healing occurs when the overriding intention of the disease has been served. As I have stated, the intention of the disease is always positive, although its physical evidence, an illness, is experienced as a negative event.

You ask, "Why would one choose negative means and negative results in order to achieve a positive intention?" Good question. In fact, it is such a fascinating phenomenon among us humans that this observation has continued to be the story plot for both fiction and actual history, be it for one person or for an entire nation since recorded time. Let us take a look at the possible script, starring a young man named Bob Brown. Bob Brown believes that he can create a business that could make him rich and improve the local economy. The story plot shows that Bob got everything he wanted and easily accomplished his dream. This television show's life would be very brief because letters of protest would pour in from viewers who would protest that their intelligence had been insulted by this lack of "realism." Advertisers would cancel financial support and of course the producers would dump the show. If on the other hand, the plot plan called for Bob to go through difficulties which make hell pale by comparison, and he almost lost his life getting to his dream, every viewer would be moved. Just about everyone who considered themselves intelligent would consider this a realistic story. The first story, the one which shows success with ease, would be dismissed as a childish fairy tale.

Now, are we still wondering why we humans choose a negative means to realize a positive intention? It is our habit to do so. It is how we keep ourselves paying attention; how we keep entertained; and it is how we *believe* that everything worthwhile can be achieved, through pain. In short, we believe in *limitations*. We are creatures of limitation and we don't believe anything good can come about without having to hack our way through them.

Is this good or bad? I can't answer for everybody, but I do know that it hurts. If it didn't hurt, there would be no need for people like me, or other doctors and healers. It is not the sphere of activity of the healer to judge the choice of disease as a tool to satisfy a positive need as good or bad, but simply to recognize that it exists. A good healer views this choice with curiosity and then proceeds to assist the patient with integrity in arriving at the positive intention, which is the gift of the disease. A good healer will also instruct the patient not to judge the disease situation. This is because the healer knows that indulging in negative emotion or negative energy motion will keep the patient even further from discovering the positive intent or to extract any good from the disease. The patient may get to this goal eventually with negative emotion, but it will be a long and unpleasant journey. And it's cost will not be confined to money alone.

Limitation is the human's game. We choose disease, a limitation, to achieve a positive end. "You've made your point, Vida. Now get on with it and tell us what this positive intention is," people quite often urge impatiently at this point.

All right then, as I said in the first section of this work, each individual is his/her own viewpoint. Therefore, each individual's intention will be their own unique creation. However, the overall intention of living life in the physical world is to live that life to the fullest. In other words, the highest intention that is common to all humans is to be the fullest expression or the best possible human being we can be in the life we are living on earth. Every other intention is a path leading to this goal and is subordinate to this overriding intention. Let's take a look at a common scenario.

You are an ambitious modern young mother and a successful corporate climber. You notice that quite often, you arrive home with a splitting headache and you are dead tired. As you arrive home, your young son runs up to you with outstretched arms, ecstatic to see Mommy. Your husband or lover beams you a smile and gives you an embrace. A wave of sheer gratitude and joy sweeps you into the kitchen and you don't remember the headache until the next day at the office. What happened?

Well, it is no "big deal" that this achiever had a headache at the end of the hard day. This is how many people, who are accustomed to living with the disease we call stress, will look on it. The "stress" is ignored until it builds into a major volcano. And it will do just that, because the disease will get your attention one way or the other, until the positive purpose is served.

If this young woman had, along with her general education, familiarity with the basic principles of metamedicine, she would have recognized the opportunity contained in her "stress." She would become curious about these headaches instead of cursing them and blaming "the job" for them. With or without the help of the healer, she would ask herself why she would choose to have the headaches, without judging and invalidating them or herself. She would then recognize that the "cure" for them is being with her loved ones, exchanging love and joy.

At home her (energy) emotion is positive and she is being true to herself, basically being a loving, joyful woman. Does this mean that she does not belong in the corporate world? Not at all. If the corporate life excites her, then she belongs there. It would not excite her unless it was also a necessary part to her full self-expression. Let us say that it does excite her. Then what? The disease "stress," that she suffers in the job setting, is still there for a positive benefit for her. From the "cue cure," it would become obvious that somehow at the job, she is functioning in a way that does not reflect her true self. She may be buying into a prevailing belief that a woman has to be abrasive and quite "masculine" to succeed in the corporate world. If she would replace this negative belief with one which says that she can succeed by being herself, she will reap spectacular results.

She may find that she can be just as effective doing her job as her real loving, joyful self, instead of some conjured up image of a dragon lady. Not only that, she will be pleasantly surprised to see that people in her work place are treating her differently by returning her love. Pretty soon, if she persists in acting herself, the emotional climate of the job site will change. In the positive atmosphere she has helped create, productivity will skyrocket and so will her career. Her "headache" will be a thing of the past. The disease, having served its intended purpose, will have no reason to remain with her.

As you can see, metamedicine principles are applicable in everyday life for healthy, joyful, positive living. If in most of this book I have referred to major illnesses as examples, it is because we human beings don't take notice of subtle messages until they knock us down flat on our backs. Also as a doctor healthy people rarely come to see me.

I would say that metamedicine principles probably enrich the relatively healthy individual the most. Such an individual still functions near peak energy (emotional) level and can be poised to use the message of any disease symptoms to catapult them even higher to superior health and living. An individual who is already debilitated from the ravages of a disease, which keeps intensifying its case because the intention is not satisfied, will first be using metamedicine to get his/her "head above the water." Fear will generally blind such an individual to seeing the treasures of the disease. In other words, it will be an uphill fight for this person to get to where he should be, had the disease not progressed so far. Nonetheless, such an individual can still reap the rewards of the disease as long as he changes his persona in a positive manner prescribed by the disease. What if he doesn't get better and dies?

The idea that an individual who dies is not healed is in contradiction with our true nature as human beings, and the transitory nature of physical existence. Human beings are energy and energy can never be created nor destroyed. It can transform. Humans do transform or translate out of physical awareness. An individual who chooses disease as the means of this passage, this translation into another energy state, deserves healing even more urgently. These persons have a very limited time during which they have to experience full expression in this life. They must come to terms with themselves and make the transition without fear and pain but with joy and power, knowing that they would always continue to exist.

Can metamedicine principle be useful to any individual who chooses not to take advantage of the positive intention of the disease? But, of course. There are as many options available to human beings as they care to imagine.

The usual scenario, where we get sick or get hurt and want to have the anatomical part fixed, has been the human approach and has been of service in keeping us alive and functioning. Even in this limited idea of health, which is the avoidance or elimination of pain, there is a lot the individual can do to bring relief to his/her pains with or without the outside help of a healer-doctor.

Take a look again in the last example of the young working mother with a headache. We notice that when she gets back to her true (emotional) energy form which is her true self, she no longer experiences headache. So it is with all pain. All pain comes from friction, from going against the grain of our true energy form. What we physically experience as pain is our brain's interpretation of this misalignment of energy. The brain then sends this information through neural pathways, the nerve fibers, to the respective anatomical part for response.

What we usually do to alleviate pain, whether we take medicines or other therapy, is to interrupt the neural pathway involved in the pain loop. A more powerful method of dealing with pain in metamedicine is to change the meaning of pain altogether at the brain level. In other words, we reprogram the human software in the brain through thought .

Next time you begin having pain, relax and think about it as just a sensation. Link the sensation with a pleasant experience. Then in your imagination, have the sensation diffuse out of your body into the surrounding air. If you do this with conviction, you will not experience what was felt previously to be a pain as such.

A similar technique is taught women for achieving painless childbirth. In a relaxed state, a woman going into labor is instructed to focus her attention on the unborn baby. She is to follow the movements of the infant in the womb with ecstatic, loving thoughts. Then she is instructed to use her breathing to relax her pelvis with each contraction. The beginning of each contraction is to serve as a cue or an anchor for her to deep-breathe and relax. The effects of this is that she does not tense up and generate friction by struggling against the contraction and the movement of the fetus. She flows with the muscular movements and therefore, experiences no pain. She has supplanted fear with love and joy for the new infant.

In relaxation response maneuvers, we are in effect aligning with energy and flowing smoothly with it. We experience no discomfort because no friction, physical or emotional has been generated.

As you can see, as long as you can understand that all pain, physical and emotional, results from frictional energy, you can design many ways of successfully preventing pain from occurring.

Does lack of pain mean health? No, because you can be painfree and still contain and suffer from a disease. If you want life to represent more to you than the mere ability to breathe air, then it is time we explore the true meaning of health or wellness.

162

10
Wellness

*"The health of the people is really the foundation
upon which all their happiness and all their
powers as a state depend."*

- Benjamin Disraeli

Health is the condition of being in total alignment, in total
harmony with the unique energy that one is. In its perfect
state, the personality does not contain any disease. Since health is
a birthright, wellness is not something one should struggle to
achieve. For this reason, I have avoided applying the term "Preventive Health" to wellness.

Preventive Health connotes a sense of fear which is in and of
itself, a negative belief. It generally lists what we must do to avoid
a disease state or what we must avoid to stay healthy. As an
example, we are told to avoid high cholesterol diets in order to keep
our hearts and blood vessels healthy and to exercise in order to avoid
obesity and premature aging. In each instance, a sense of struggle
is implied. In Preventive Health, wellness becomes something we
have to struggle for or suffer to achieve. Such a negative attitude
runs counter to health. The very measures that are prescribed to
promote well-being, such as certain diets and exercises, soon
become a source of stress and guilt. Some individuals actually

manage to create compulsions out of these ideas, thus creating stress out of that which was meant to function as a stress control measure. The resulting sports injuries, nutritional problems and emotional instability keep sports medicine doctors and other medical practitioners fully employed.

Metamedicine says that since health is a birthright, we can simply choose to stay healthy. Easier said than done? It appears so but it really isn't, if we reconstruct our persona make-up of belief, emotion, and thought. The first area we must revamp is the belief system.

As humans, we harbor a belief system that expects decay and malfunction in the physical body. We also consciously or unconsciously subscribe to a belief system that says: no pain no gain. We believe that it requires pain and struggle to keep healthy. This system of negative belief, or self-invalidation, is one of the most pervasive sources of all of our ill-health.

Our scientists and medical professionals are beginning to recognize the power of emotion in health and disease. Quite often, manipulation of emotional energy is the only therapeutic measure available in illnesses where we have not as yet discovered any cure as such. AIDS and other immune related diseases are perfect examples. This is the major avenue for the so-called miracle cures. Proper early education about emotion as a state of personal energy and skill in maintenance of emotional balance would generally guarantee us generations of disease-free children. Emotional balance is of paramount importance in health.

Neuroscientists have discovered that every thought we hold "re-wires" the brain. That means that while the blueprint of the basic circuitry of the brain is determined by belief, it is thought that does the actual wiring by making the connections between the various neurons and dendrites in the brain. To say that thoughts are things is basically a valid way of describing this idea. As Einstein has elegantly shown us, matter and energy are both expressions of the same thing. The brain controls and directs all activities in the physical body which I have described simply as the brain's sensory channels and supporting organs. Need I now convince anyone that your thoughts can keep your body healthy or sick? Thoughts are things. Remember this during each moment of time, because the quality of one's life depends on this knowledge.

By revamping our beliefs about health, maintaining an emotional balance and keeping only those thoughts which promote our highest good, we can remain in our natural perfect state which equates with perfect health.

Early health education is a necessity for every culture that manifests disease and that means just about every civilization on the planet Earth. In the United States alone, health related spending which is tantamount to spending on disease is about 12 percent of our gross national product and the figures keep rising each year. The cost in terms of human energy and productivity cannot be estimated.

In fact, it is ludicrous to watch the government and finance people cry about the cost of health. Human health *is* the source of the nation's economy.

A healthy human being is one who is living life on Earth to its fullest expression, that is, as the best possible human being he or she is capable of being. Such healthy individuals are, therefore, fully empowered and fully creative. All wealth, everything in the economy, comes from creativity. The nation's economy is the same as the creativity and energy of its people.

Need I convince anybody about the importance of health education? Has it occurred to you by now that metamedicine is largely an educational process? The metamedicine concept that disease is a tool for learning has a flip side. Metamedicine is a learning process, be it therapeutic or instructional. When should the educational process begin? In metamedicine we recommend that the educational process begin even prior to birth. The unborn infant is a self-aware consciousness and the parents would benefit from an interaction such as the following:

The parents can communicate verbally with the unborn infant in loving ways. They can tell the infant about all the beautiful and positive things in the world. Studies have shown that unborn babies can hear. Babies are very telepathic. They tune into their mother's emotional state. I consider a relaxed loving environment the greatest gift parents can give to the unborn or to new infants. It is important to be sincere when communicating verbally with the unborn infant. For it is just as intelligent a creature as the parent, maybe more so. My husband and I always talked to our infant daughter as if she were an adult and she never exhibited "baby talk." People were commenting on how intelligent and adult-like she was in her speech when she was only two years old. A few were startled by what they called her "eerie," grown-up talk.

The parents must make very effort to avoid any stress. Music with sixty beats per minute, such as the Baroque music, especially the slow or largo movements, has a very relaxing effect on all concerned. For some reason, this rhythm has the effect of a sonic massage on the body and the mind. The body relaxes and the mind becomes alert.

I have already described a pain free labor. This also keeps birth trauma to a minimum. It is important that all events surrounding the birth of the infant be as stress free and joyful as possible.

As the child grows up, he or she must be exposed to as positive an environment as is possible. The single most important thing that children need to be taught is self-empowerment. They should be made to believe that they are as powerful as they need to be to get anything they want without hurting anybody else or themselves in order to do so. Generations of children who believe this will make war obsolete. It is possible that by this mechanism alone we could have peace in the world.

If like most people young and old, you missed out on a healthy beginning, you can still learn the ways of wellness. I will describe some of the tools available for this quest. So please, read on.

11
Tools for Health

Wellness is experienced as a certain energy in us. It is either felt as an external physical energy or as an internal emotional energy state. Most people have at the very least, a vague sense of what they consider being "well." A lot of them will describe wellness as lack of pain and the possession of a certain level of strength as well as feeling reasonably happy or not feeling bad. Just about everyone describes health as a form of energy state, whether they realize it or not.

Recall that I have described human beings as conscious energy. Each person is a unique energy vibratory state of beingness. It can be said that each individual is a certain energy vibratory signature which is the vibratory pattern of energy that is unique to them. Once individuals sense this energy level, they will recognize it as their true state of beingness. They will feel it as a sense of completeness and peace. It is at this level that the individual is said to be on the path of his or her true self.

It is at the state of the person's core energy vibration that he/she is able to let his/her energy flow easily because there is no friction. He/she finds it easy to perform the life activities that are in line, in tune, or that are compatible with this energy frequency. This individual accomplishes things with ease and there is no disease. Also, at this point, recognize that even though we have a signature vibratory level, we can vary it at will to match any energy state that we wish to be. This can be negative or positive because the choice is *completely* up to us.

Excitement

The quickest way to reach our signature vibratory energy level, to reach any other positive energy level, or to become emotionally balanced, is by doing what excites us the most; by doing that which gives us the most peace at each moment. Excitement represents the physical translation of the vibratory energy of the path that we are on and the life that we are. It indicates who we are. Does this mean that there is one specific thing we are meant to do or be in life? No. We can do many things, we can have many careers, and they can all be a part of the common purpose or mission of one's life. That purpose is to live one's life to the fullest. The actions that excite us; that hold our interest or feel the most right to us, are those which are in line with this purpose. These actions can vary from moment to moment. What they will have in common is that they will all be methods of expressing one's primary purpose in life. All of these actions must be performed with integrity. None of this is meant to say that one's purpose in life is preordained. It isn't. The choices are infinite and, best of all, the choice is up to you.

Does this mean that indulging one's self, like drinking and eating excessively is being on one's path? Check the definition of integrity to determine the answer to this question. I'll state the definition again: integrity means knowing that one is as powerful as one needs to be to get whatever one wants in life without hurting himself/herself or anybody else in order to do so. Therefore, any type of abuse, of one's self or of others, is not compatible with being on one's true path.

Excitement is then the momentum that moves you in the direction of what you are about. When you are doing what it is that arrests your attention, that excites you at the moment, above and beyond everything else you could possibly be doing at that time, you generally lose track of time. So excitement runs hand in hand with:

Living In The Moment

Full involvement in the "now" means that one is focusing full attention on the experiences of the moment. This is what is called being in "up time" in the phraseology of Neurolinguistic Programming. Here you are not involved in internal dialogue, that is, you are not talking to yourself. You are not judging anything. You are just keeping all your sensory channels occupied. You are not thinking about the past, neither are you contemplating the future. You are using your entire attention to savor the life of here and now. Try it for about five minutes. Walk around your yard or your neighborhood. If you have never practiced being in the now, or being in "up time," I suggest you pick a time when you are unlikely to be interrupted. You will be amazed at how many details you will recognize for the first time. You will feel as if you are seeing the places for the first time. Everything will seem to come to your vision in brighter focus. You will hear sounds you never heard before, like the ripple of a soft breeze over leaves on trees. The sights, sounds and smells will appear so tangible to you that it will feel as if you can feel them brush against your skin. Time stands still.

When you are doing what excites you the most and you are fully enjoying it in the present, in the everlasting "now," you will not notice the passage of time. In my novel, "Rousing the Gods," I wrote about a woman who hadn't aged a day in twenty years, when she went insane and stopped noticing the passage of time. It would be intriguing to research into the physiologic effects of refusing to acknowledge the passage of time in human beings.

Living in the present and doing what excites one the most does not leave any room or interest for self-judgement or invalidation of oneself and the events of one's life. Being fully involved in this way gets you to approach each experience with curiosity as the events of your life evolve. Life becomes an exciting adventure and because you are enjoying yourself so much, you won't be aware of situations and conditions in your life which other onlookers would judge to be negative. People watching from the sidelines would think, "Poor

169

John, he's working his fingers to the bone. Why does he strive so hard?" John would have no idea what the fuss is all about. He is having so much fun! And so without working at it, you naturally practice unconditional acceptance.

Unconditional Love and Acceptance

Individuals who are truly occupied at doing what excites them enjoy such a high energy state that they would not choose to judge or invalidate themselves or other people. Here is why. Invalidation or negative judgement requires negative energy. To judge, you would have to be identifying with the negativity of the negative judgement. In other words, it takes one to know one. There is no room in the high emotional states of unconditional acceptance for invalidations.

Unconditional acceptance is the highest form of acceptance of responsibility for everything in one's life. Therefore, these individuals know their power over every event in their lives, because they know that they can always change that which they choose to own. They no longer blame anyone, not even God, for events in their lives. They discover the secret of true power: unconditional love for themselves and others in their world. They find that loving others unconditionally is a gift they give themselves because it allows them to exist in the energy climate of ecstatic joy and full power. These are the individuals who can create heaven out of any hell, when they have it in their belief system that they desire to do so. They are the embodiment of the saying that if life gives you lemons you can make lemonade.

Belief Versus Fear

Many people have begun to recognize the connection between what they believe and what they physically experience. Every superstition of ancient cultures is based on the idea that whatever people believe will happen to them. I remember the "new pot" ritual very well.

As a child growing up in West Africa, one of the most exciting events in daily living is the purchase of a new pot for a child at the village market by the mother. In those days, all the water needed in the household had to be fetched from the wilderness streams and fountains. We would trot down the ravine into the river valley to fetch special, "sweet" drinking water from the sandy fountains.

As you got older and stronger, you graduated to carrying larger and larger pots on your head for this purpose. As children, we looked forward to acquiring a new pot. There was nothing more delicious than the aroma and taste of water stored in a clay pot which had newly arrived from the kiln. We would admire the fresh decorative art work on the belly of the pot. The new pot was perfect in every way, with no chips or cracks anywhere on its surface.

As the mother hands this new gift to the child, every adult watches carefully as the child handles the pot. If the child voices fear that he is afraid the pot will break, someone will usually snatch the pot away from him. He will be yelled at and ordered to renounce the belief immediately. It is only after he does so and with apologies that he is allowed to own the pot. Adults swear that unless he renounced his fear, which is a negative belief, that the pot would never make it home from the stream with the boy. And you know what? It happened exactly that way every time. Our people had become acutely aware of self-fulfilling prophesies.

Belief and fear carry equal power. They are simply polar opposites. The common element to both ideas is trust. Belief is trust in the positive, and fear is trust in the negative. A person will experience what he believes the strongest or what he fears the most. A person fleeing toward a goal out of fear will attain that goal only with the greatest effort. The individual who craves wealth, out of a desperate fear of poverty, might reach his goal but the effort required would make the Horatio Alger story seem like child's play.

Most people are usually unaware of having certain beliefs that get in the way of their progress. This is no cause for alarm. Instead of anxiety, one should allow it to arouse one's curiosity. You can begin to wonder what beliefs you could be holding that are being reflected as a negative experience in your life .

Remember that all a belief represents is a reference to what you think is true for you. Therefore, when I find myself going from illness to illness, one thing I know right away is that I don't care for ill health. Then I ask myself, "Why am I allowing my body to be sick?" I reserve all judgement, including cursing my luck, and I put on my special hat. I have named it my "curiosity" hat and when I am really taken by fascination, I'll call it my "sorcerer's" hat. I put on this hat and go hunting in the fields of my belief system. Quite often, I find that the image I hold of myself did not ooze vitality and health.

Once when I was in peak physical condition, I came down with the lousiest cold I can ever remember. Naturally, I was disgusted. I had been exercising regularly, eating right and generally behaving myself. I complained about how I deserved to he healthy because I took pains to keep my body in good shape. Right after I got tired of feeling bad and decided that I had more interesting things to do than lie in bed and nurse the cold, I remembered the cause. I remembered that everyone in our office had come down with a cold, and I recall thinking, "I wonder how long it will take before I catch it too." Then laughed. I laughed because without even the benefit of another person's suggestion, I had bought into a belief that said that I would catch the cold; it would just be a matter of time! And catch the cold I did.

What did I learn about myself from this illness? What was the positive intent of my cold? For one thing, I learned that the accepted medical standards of cause and effect do not necessarily have to hold true for me. They would prove true for me only if I believed in them. This happens all the time. If it wasn't so, doctors would have a very short life. Think about how many contagious diseases doctors and medical workers handle each day. Their major immunity and protection against these contagious diseases is their belief system. It never occurs to the majority of them that they could come down with the disease. Mark you, they are aware of the probability of catching the disease. They are certainly exposed to the viruses/

bacteria more frequently than the majority of our population. Nonetheless, they do not believe that they will contract the illness. After all, they are the "healers." You can use the same power of belief to inoculate yourself against ill health.

The second thing I learned from that cold was not to turn my back on fear. Let me explain. I was afraid of the cold. I was afraid that I was going to catch it but I didn't do anything about the fear and it got the better of me because I did come down with a cold. Remember what I said earlier: the events in our life are governed by either what we belief most or what we fear most strongly. Well, what can one do about a fear? Before exploring the answer to this question, let's take a look first at what fear is. Fear is designed as a quick physiologic reaction to any event or idea that threatens the organism's life or its survival. We respond physiologically by quickly producing more adrenalin, which kicks up our heart rate, and we are alert and ready to take action to preserve ourselves. This is the so called "fight or flight" reaction. Then the fear or fright reaction is over. If the feeling of fear persists beyond the brief interval it is designed to act as an alerting mechanism it becomes a negative judgement, something that we believe is bad. We fear something only when we have judged that thing to be negative. Anxiety is in the same category as fear, except that anxiety is more or less nonspecific.

Knowing this, you can see that one of the worst things you can do about a fear is negating it by either denying it or running away from it. Negating the fear in this way adds even more fuel to its negativity, giving it more force or power. Therefore, we suggest that first and foremost, you accept the fear as the friend it was designed to be in the first place. In other words, you face the fear.

The second thing to do about fear is to get curious about it. Take a good look at it from every angle and find out what it is all about and what it is doing for you. Once you exercise this prerogative to use curiosity, you will discover that the fear will dissipate. It won't hold your interest and attention much longer. Then, if you are really persistent and care to do so, you can replace it with a positive belief.

As long as one remembers to use fear as a friendly device, something that taps one on the shoulder to alert him/her to possibilities, the negative effects of fear will not be experienced. It is only when we do not allow fear to do its job, and instead judge it, that it becomes a menace.

For fears we have nursed into monstrous proportions up to the point where we cannot get them out of our minds, we can apply the techniques described in the section on "Mind Magic."

> "A coward dies a thousand times before his death,
> a brave man dies but once."
> — William Shakespeare

Diet and Exercise

"Ah, delicious physicality! ... Enjoy, enjoy, enjoy..."
- Ancient/Future Wisdom

In recent years, people who come to our centers for their annual physical examinations quite often request information on diet and exercise. This demonstration of interest in actively maintaining the body in a certain condition of fitness is a radical shift in our society's concept of health. In the past, the same individuals coming for their annual check-up were quite content to know that there were "no major problems" with their bodies. Virtually none showed any degree of interest in our nutrition and exercise pamphlets. Now, they all want to know what they should do to stay trim. At first I thought this was just another fad, in line with the American society's obsession with youth. I was wrong. Recently, what all the candidates for the metamedicine weight control program listed as their number one reason for desiring to lose weight was, "to feel good about myself." The second most important reason they gave was the satisfaction of looking good. It is exciting to watch people's attitude towards health shift from fear of disease to a positive vision of their bodies. Another example of our societies shift in emphasis is seen at many large hotels. One doesn't have to be ancient to remember when these hotels advertised only their restaurants and bars. Now most of them have health clubs and are proud to offer more health-conscious menus in their restaurants.

There is no one correct way to achieve and maintain the human body in a healthy condition. If there was, there would only be one person in the world, and there are millions and millions of people. A basic understanding of what the body is and how it functions will act as a guide in designing any program of activities, including diet and exercise, which can assist in achieving and maintaining health. Based on this knowledge, we can create some exciting ways of engaging in fun-filled activities which promote health. So, let us take a look again at the integrated view of the human body.

175

I have described the body as simply the sensory channels and supporting organs of the brain. To keep our focus on this idea, I will not go into the details of human physiology and anatomy. There are many excellent text books on these subjects.

Metamedicine defines health as the state of being in total alignment with the one's unique energy. In this state, you cannot contain any disease and you become the fullest expression of the best possible human being you are capable of being. Can you imagine what life would be like if you were the best possible person you could be? You would most certainly be doing things that give you the most joy; you would be happy and wealthy in every way. These are the real values or meaning of health. When you decide that these are primary values that you desire and deserve as a human being, then you will embrace any habits and activities that will lead you to health with joy and gratitude.

It is important to approach any activity which is undertaken for promotion of health from an integrated idea of the self, or the total personality. The belief system, emotional energy, thought and physical activity must be called into play and blended to achieve the values we seek in being healthy. This idea is not just an airy philosophy. We have arrived at the total approach to diet and exercise from observations and from experience.

Without the proper emotional (energy) climate, every diet and exercise regimen will become an uphill fight and will ultimately fail. Likewise, with a defective belief system, the most powerfully built body will succumb to debilitating diseases and the people will cry, "This is not fair!" In fact, I have had many obese patients who found it impossible to lose weight beyond a certain point on the weight scale until their belief system was overhauled. After we changed their beliefs, they succeeded in reaching their goals.

I will not cover specific dietary regimens and exercise programs here, because there are many excellent books and programs on these subjects. Research is turning out more information on nutrition all the time, and exercise physiologists and sports medicine specialists are refining fitness with great skill. I will give some general guidelines of an approach to diet and exercise.

1. The purpose of living in a physical world as a physical body is to experience physicality and to enjoy that physicality. Therefore, the number one prerequisite for any exercise program is enjoyment. You must enjoy having a body and moving that body. Take every part of the body gracefully through its natural range of motion with joy. To understand what I am saying, watch little children at play. They find great fun in moving every limb and with every motion of their bodies.

2. As you move, engage all your sensory channels. Smell the air, fill up the lungs and let the air out completely. Let your vision hungrily take in every detail of your environment, and listen to the sounds of the world and of your own body. Embrace every tree, shrub, animal, and person in your imagination with your joy. Think with gratitude for the privilege of experiencing physical life.

3. If you walk, move with grace and imagine moving with agility, even if you are convinced that your joints are stiff. If you run, run like a child—with joy. You will be amazed with your speed and ease of motion, if you do.

4. Stretch and dance. Dance is the song of the body. It is beauty in motion. It doesn't matter how you dance, just dance. Let your inner music move you and dance only to your feelings.

5. Breathing is the key to energizing the body. It also is the key to relaxation. It must be done without effort. Empty out the lungs completely. Then, let the air rush in to naturally occupy the empty spaces. Go watch infants breathe and you will see what I mean. Instead of coffee breaks, take breathing breaks and surprise yourself with vitality.

6. Simple, natural foods: vegetables, fruits, carbohydrates and nuts combined with lesser amounts of meats and fish, and washed down with copious amounts of fresh water remains as nourishing to us today as they were to our ancestors who, although they bragged of their hunting prowess, had to be content with fruits and vegetables more often than not.

7. Your eating programs should be tailored to support your energy. Eat only the types of food you need, in the quantities that your physical activity levels will require.

8. It is important that you taste the food. Savor every morsel, and if you do this, you will not have a tendency to overeat.

9. Do not use your stomach as a timepiece. Eat only when you need to. Less is better, at least in the United States. This may or may not be valid in other poorer countries.

10. If you are not eating for energy, you are eating for entertainment or some other reason. Wear your integrity to such a feast in order to circumvent self-abuse.

If you treat your body with respect and love, it will allow you the maximum enjoyment of physicality. So, eat, move, play and above all, enjoy.

12
Mind Magic

Nikola Tesla, who is perhaps the greatest inventor of all times, produced seven hundred inventions, including alternating current systems, neon and fluorescent lighting as well as basic electric motors, without bothering with the usual trial and error methods. He constructed every detail mentally in his imagination, tested the devices in his inner vision before they were ever put to production. So tangible were these imagined motors to him, that he would often point them out in the empty air for his bewildered friends to see. Was Tesla insane? No, he was just an individual who had activated and trained his capacity to work his imagination with precision. What stands him apart from most of mankind was his ability to give equal validity to things in his imagination and those that are physically real. In other words, to him the world of the imagination was just as real as the physical world. Tesla created things in his imagination and then proceeded to see them become physical.

We all do the same thing, except that Tesla did them fully consciously and we do them without being consciously aware that we are doing so. Whatever we do, we must think about it first. In thinking about it, we do one or more of three things. We may have a mental image of us doing the thing; we may hear ourselves saying something about doing the thing; and we may have feelings about doing the same thing. In either case, there is an internal process that takes place before the actual physical action. You won't be aware of this unless you deliberately slow the process down and pay conscious attention to it. We do this so fast and so naturally that it long ago became an unconscious process. We say, "Well, I did what was on my mind; I told myself that it is something I've got to do; or I felt it was something I needed to do," etc., etc. These are the ways we describe fashioning, viewing and hearing things in our imagination prior to physically performing the actions.

The human imagination is the unlimited dimension of space-time where all realities are possible. It is the screen where we project everything we wish to see in our physical world. It is also the space wherein we can change everything including ourselves. Imagination is what bridges all the fragments and all the worlds of energy described as consciousness. The imagination therefore contains unlimited potential for human creation internally and externally.

Human children live freely in their imagination and lend validity to all events in this sphere, especially when they are very young. I recall how utterly amazed my four-year-old daughter was when she discovered that her babysitter did not know that her stuffed animals could talk! It occurred to me then that she wouldn't be surprised at all if those stuffed animals sat at the dinner table and ate with us. Such is the power of a child's imagination.

As we become adults and limit our explorations to the analytical or rational regions of the mind, we alienate our natural gift of having experience in the imaginary world. There are a few individuals who as adults are successful in tenaciously holding onto this ability. These are people we call geniuses. These individuals also have an uncommon ability to keep other adults from knowing the full extent of their lives in this other reality—the reality of the imaginary world. Otherwise people would label them insane. These gifted people know that in order for us to express our full potential as beings, we must harness our powers of imagination.

Nikola Tesla enjoyed a fortunate childhood. Not only was he encouraged to use his imagination, his mother actually purposefully and consistently trained him early in visualization and played ESP games with him. Tesla grew up with an early, practical education in total mind power. This educational process consisted of using belief to lend validity to mental imagery earlier on, and later using the power of emotional energy and thought to recreate the imagery in the physical world. What are we the rest of adult mankind who were taught, "It is just your imagination, it is not real," to do? Simply this: learn and change, because change is the only constant in the universe.

Unlike Tesla's mother who knew by instinct that things seen in the imagination are real, but had no way to prove it, we now have scientific proof or explanation for the validity of the reality of those things we imagine.

Our leading neuroscientists have discovered that visual images and sensory impressions generated in the brain are holographic in nature. Recall that the brain is the physical representation of the mind. A hologram is a three-dimensional image projected into space that one cannot visually distinguish from the real life object. If you cut a holographic image of an orange projected in space into two, you will get two complete three-dimensional holographic images of the orange. If you cut each into thousands of pieces, each piece would still be a complete holographic image of the orange. Because of the holographic nature of the brain, each brain cell contains the information of the whole brain. The brain's holographic image is a by-product of an electrical and chemical process.

Quantum physics states that the basic building block of all matter is electromagnetic wave energy. As we have seen, if matter is broken down to the level of electrons and even more basic components, the ultimate form will be electromagnetic (light) wave energy. In other words, electromagnetic waves give rise to atoms, which ultimately we experience as matter.

Those familiar with the production of a physical hologram know that the patterns recorded on the undeveloped film plate are generated when a reference beam and an object beam of split laser light collide or interact with each other. The film plate is then developed. To reconstruct the object hologram, a second reference beam is directed on the developed film plate at the same angle as the original reference beam. As it illuminates the plate, a hologram of the object is projected into space.

Impressions from our sensory channels are recorded in the brain as electrical and chemical impulses. These impulses converging on the brain cells are stored as interacting patterns throughout the brain. The brain therefore, functions as an organic film plate.

In the brain, electromagnetic wave energy serves as the laser light. The eye serves as the object beam and all the other senses—touch, smell, sound, taste, in addition to emotion—become the reference beam. A hologram of an original experience can be triggered by an appropriate sensory reference beam. A three-dimensional mental image of the experience can then be visualized in the space of the imagination. This hologram is an electromagnetic wave form that possesses energy and can be perceived as matter. This is why we say that things in the imagination are just as valid as things in the physical world. Both are composed of the same basic building blocks—electromagnetic energy waves.

There is a principle in physics called the law of electromagnetic energy. It states that an electrical energy field will simultaneously produce an attraction force—a magnetic field. Herein lies the power of vision in our imagination to create changes in our reality. The visions we create in our imagination—our mind's screen and space, will generate attraction forces. Whatever we vividly imagine will become attracted to us. Whatever we sense with clarity, purpose and emotional energy, will create a strong electromagnetic field that will begin to attract forces in the outside world to us. This is the meaning of the universal law: what one puts out is what one gets back, or "as ye sow so shall ye reap."

The human brain and body react in the same manner to both a vividly imagined idea and an actual experience in physical reality. If you fear disease more than you trust in health, you are in effect generating images of ill health, whether you are aware of it or not. Therefore, you will attract all the negative forces which will culminate in your being ill. If you are ill already, you will attract forces that will keep you that way or make you worse and even contribute to your death.

In metamedicine, one of the first interventions instituted is fear control. This can be done concurrently with prescribed medical management of the illness. Quite often, in non-life threatening illnesses, a basic metamedicine explanation of what a disease is may be enough to allay the anxiety or fear of the patient. This is especially true for those individuals who accept responsibility for their disease and approach their illnesses with curiosity and a positive attitude. For these individuals, while they are learning what the disease is all about, they also speed up resolution of the illness by making use of the power of mental imagery. We instruct them to visualize the affected body part as completely healed and healthy. They are taught to evoke the imagery using all their sensory channels and infuse it with the power of positive emotional energy. In other words, they activate the full force of their belief on the vision of the healthy body they created in their imagination. This quite often results in accelerated resolution of the illness, along with the complete healing of the disease. Such powerful vision attracts and compels the body's healing resources to come to the rescue. Reports abound of miraculous recoveries and remissions in cancer patients who use imagery in healing themselves.

When fear of the disease or fear of death has become an overpowering force on patients, we take them through a generic fear neutralizing procedure as follows:

After helping these individuals get into as relaxed a state as possible, we instruct them to think about their fear and allow all the negative emotions associated with it—their anguish, anger, bitterness and pain to rise to the surface from the depths of their being. We then ask them to incarnate all this into the most disgusting, hideous creature they can imagine. Next, we ask them to transform themselves in their imagination into an exact duplicate image of this creature, but twice as big. In this form, they face the hideous creature and allow rage against all that this creature represents to overtake them. At the peak of this rage, they bite off the creature's head and watch the blood spurt out of its headless body. Then they let their own creature bodies become radiant and crystalline. From their crystalline eyes, they will shoot out laser-like beams of light which ignites the creature and burns it to ashes. They then watch as rain falls on the ashes and rivulets of rain water carry the ashes away into the fields. Next, they watch green grass grow where the rain water has deposited the ashes. Then we have them take deep breaths and they wake from this trance with a feeling of peace.

After this exercise, these individuals do not have the fear anymore. If you do this exercise with anything that causes you much fear, you will verify for yourself its incredible power in eliminating that fear.

Once fear is out of the way, we can then investigate the disease in a more resourceful emotional climate to discover the causative negative beliefs. Neurolinguistic Programming can then be used to change these beliefs. Powerful visualization exercises are encouraged as a tool for accelerated healing of the illness, but sometimes we find that this is difficult for some individuals. The usual cause of such difficulty is habitual stress. A significant percentage of adults in this society do not know what it is to be relaxed, and a majority of this group do not know how to take a deep breath. What do these abilities have to do with the capacity to form a vision in the imagination? Everything. And here's why.

When we are frightened, angry or just plain tense, our muscles contract and blood is diverted from our heads and limbs to the heart which is induced to beat faster by the adrenalin released into the circulation. This enables us to act in an emergency. This whole event is called a fight or flight reaction. It is a reflex action as old as man himself. Because the blood flow is diverted away from our limbs and brains, our hands and feet may feel cold and sweaty when we are in a fearful situation. By the same token, some men and women faint during extreme fright because the blood flow is diverted away from their brains.

During the state of tension, the brain which is relatively deprived of its usual blood supply must continue to control the body parts, such as the heart. Therefore, the vital demands on the brain are great, and such creative activities as mental imagery is abandoned. Stress is a condition of chronic anxiety, worry and doubt which robs the brain of adequate blood flow and its attendant oxygenation. Therefore in stress conditions, people find it difficult to create mental imagery.

Think about a time when you searched for something ordinary that you know you cannot lose, like a key. You become upset and tear your house or office apart looking for it. After you get tired of being agitated, you settle down, having given up the struggle. Just about the moment you stopped thinking about the key, a thought comes into your mind and you get up and automatically find the key. Sometimes the key is right where you always kept it, or even in your own pocket, and you feel quite embarrassed. Many students have a similar experience taking examinations. They report that quite often they would feel the answer to a question at the tip of their tongues but are unable to recall it in the heat of the examination. After the examination is over and they turn in their papers, as they step outside, the answer would pop into their heads. In each case, anxiety and stress deprived the brain of its normal blood flow and oxygen and so they were unable to visualize the answers to the problems which they knew all along. Anxiety had created a sort of "short circuit" in their brain.

To achieve effective and purposeful creation of imagery in our minds, it will be necessary to train oneself in proper breathing techniques and deliberate muscular and mental relaxation. Rhythmic breathing, such as taught in many yoga exercises, enhances concentration, slows the pulse rate and is invaluable in achieving total body relaxation.

In metamedicine encounters, we begin all sessions by instructing the individual on effective breathing. We place much emphasis on breathing because we have observed that breathing to a specific rhythm pattern is one of the fastest and easiest ways of increasing the awareness of internal states of consciousness as well as relaxing the body.

We associate breathing with imagined colors and calibrate the depth and rate of breathing with various colors. We also record the kinesthetic or body sensations associated with each color. Quite often, we have observed that the color that is accompanied by the greatest subjective sense of body relaxation is also the color that is associated with the largest volumes and slowest rates of respiration. A most interesting finding is that in almost all cases, the most effective color for relaxation and breathing is different from the individual's favorite color. An individual whose color preference is blue, may breathe and relax best imagining the color red.

Once adequate relaxation is obtained, we assist the patients in creating an internal imagery of themselves as having completely recovered from their illnesses and enjoying healthy living. Some patients are able to do this. Others will complain that they have never been able to "see in their imagination." We assume that they are able to envision things, except that they are not aware that they are doing so. Most individuals who have difficulty creating a vision in the imagination are people whose main method of accessing and coding information is through the auditory or kinesthetic channels. People who are visually oriented can envision images more readily.

Individuals who are primarily kinesthetic and who have trouble visualizing, are encouraged to access the imagined internal and external feelings which they would have if they were completely healthy. As they completely associate themselves with these feelings or become lost in these feelings, they will become aware that they are also seeing or sensing images of themselves in a state of health. The more intense their feelings are, the more vivid will be the vision they experience. In the same way, primarily auditory individuals can access the sounds they associate with a healthy state. It can be the voice of people commenting on how well they look, and it can be the sounds or music associated with the activity they do in a healthy state. This can be intensified up to a point where they are able to sense images of themselves as completely healthy.

If we recall the holographic nature of the brain, it will not be surprising that we can create mental imagery by accessing all sensory channels and emotion internally. Recall that these serve as a reference beam in creating a hologram of whatever it is we want to view in our imagination. The vision of health thus created must be powered by positive emotions of joy and gratitude. As the patients strongly associate these emotions with a vivid healthly image of themselves, they discover several things. The first thing they notice is that they feel physically stronger. Then, they will report that they no longer need quite as much medication to be pain-free or comfortable. Their appetites improve and they find new interest in following or rejecting a prescribed medical regimen. All in all, they notice that they are getting well.

We come across some patients and individuals who are so chronically tense, that they have no concept of what relaxation means. I remember one woman in her late thirties who told me she did not recall ever not being tense. She said that as soon as she got out of bed in the morning, she would begin worrying about everything—her children, her husband, the dog and their finances. The tension got worse as the day progressed. Obviously she relaxed enough to fall asleep at night, but she chose not to allow herself to remember that. She had come to our ambulatory surgery center for a hernia surgery and she successfully worked her tension into panic proportions. She could not concentrate enough to carry out simple instructions on breathing and muscular relaxation. So, I resorted to pharmacological methods.

"Mrs. Edwards," I said, "I am going to give you an injection which will help you calm down and feel better. Now, I want you to pay close attention to your body—from the tip of your toes to the top of your head. You must inform me about any changes you notice and stay awake so you can talk about it." I gave her an intravenous dose of a mild sedative.

"My limbs feel real heavy," she said rather plaintively after awhile.

"Well, don't fight it," I instructed her. "Relax and enjoy that feeling."

I taught her deep rhythmic breathing and after a few minutes, she began to laugh and with tears in her eyes commented, "I have never felt this good, ever."

"Keep track of all your feelings because I am going to have you repeat them after your surgery, and you will also be doing them over and over again until you can do them without thinking about it," I told her. Her surgery was done under local anesthesia.

Post-operatively in the recovery room, she was very calm and relaxed. She remembered and was able to access the sequence of her relaxation routine without the drug. She thought that she was still under the influence of the drug.

"No, Mrs. Edwards, you are doing it all by yourself," I assured her. "That injection served just to remind your body of what it already knows. Now you remember how to get relaxed."

"Well, I guess I didn't get just my hernia fixed," she commented as she was being discharged. "I got my head fixed too!" She was able to do the visualization exercises with ease, and she healed rapidly.

I have never been an avid fan of classical music. In fact for a long time, I would only tolerate the sound. It is a trait my husband attributes to my "primitive" upbringing. However, I did notice that some Baroque music had a strange effect on me. It was as if against my will, my mind succumbed to a vague but strong appeal in this music. Almost grudgingly I began to collect music by sixteenth to eighteenth century composers like Bach, Vivaldi, Corelli, and Handel. I got into the habit of playing these tapes at surgery. I did this to break the monotony of long, tedious surgical cases, or at least so I thought at first. I could not imagine playing them at home for entertainment. So I played them at the operating room, figuring that nobody would mind since the music contained no voice or words. Then something strange happened. The usual operating room stress-charged atmosphere changed. It was as if the surgeons, the nurses and the patients were receiving a massage. A vague peace took the edge off the stress and everyone began noticing the difference. "Dr. Baron, where's your music?" the nurses would ask whenever I came around.

Those largo (slow) movements of the Baroque concertos have become a standard fixture in our operating rooms. The body tends to melt into relaxation when exposed to the rhythm of sixty beats per minute. I find that all I had to do most of the time was to have the patient breathe with the music. I don't have to instruct them in relaxation or even urge them to concentrate. As they listen, their bodies obey the sonic patterns and their stress gives way to full body relaxation. It provides the doctors and the medical staff with a meditation interlude in the hassle that we call modern living. And what exactly is meditation?

Meditation

Most people think of meditation as a way to quiet the internal dialogue (that constant chatter in our minds), in order to achieve control of our thoughts. People have devised many methods of meditating, ranging from focusing on a word or chanting a mantra to embarking on spectacular trips into the universes of the imagination. All agree that relaxation of the body is an integral part of meditation and is also the result of what is judged to be a successful meditation. Many describe meditation in mystical symbology as a type of journey into the center of one's self, and those with a penchant for rituals would actually sit and contemplate their belly buttons or other parts of their anatomy for hours. All agree that they emerge from meditation refreshed and renewed. There is no one correct procedure for performing meditation. The ways of meditating are as infinite as the human imagination and they are all as valid as any other realities one can create.

Recall from quantum physics that all holographic vision is composed of electromagnetic waves—the same energy as basic matter. That which we envision with our mind, in our imagination, can be *real*-ized just as matter is realized, because it is *real* energy. What differentiates it from solid matter is that we lend validity to solid matter. In other words, we validate with our belief system that matter is real in a solid manner. Without this definition of matter as that which is solid and so exclusively real, in this way, we can just acknowledge that both the envisioned image and the matter we see in our regular world are both valid. They are simply alternate forms of reality. The solid one we are familiar with in our everyday world is designated as a physical reality, and the envisioned image is in alternate or other reality. All *real*ities are valid. They exist. This is why we label them physical reality and nonphysical or alternate reality. Australian aborigines and the bushmen of the Kalahari have achieved this realization to a much greater extent than modern man. Language is usually explicit. Language describes what we (the brain) experience(s) so there are no mistakes in communication in that sense.

All methodologies which we employ to assist in going into the meditative state, are intended to allow the mentality, the thought, to detach from our physical reality in order to explore the larger expanse of the alternate realities of our mind's imagination. The common intention of this exploration is to seek, or get in alignment, with one's core vibratory energy state. When an individual is aligned with his/her signature vibratory frequency, this individual does not contain disease. We arbitrarily call this equilibrium condition the "zero-rest point." Most people also refer to it as the "center of the self" and the act of being at this point, as "centering oneself." A by-product of being centered is that one experiences the unlimited energy of the core self. This is why people find themselves energized by meditation.

It is important to recognize that what we are actually doing during meditation is allowing ourselves to expand into our greater awareness, even though it may appear that all we are doing is controlling and directing our thoughts. It doesn't matter by what method we approach meditation, be it by prayer, chanting or other physical activity, the result is the same. We journey into an expanded awareness to the center of our core vibrational energy frequency. In this expanded idea of ourselves, we can find answers to questions which are not accessible to us in the limited outer consciousness of physical reality. When we meditate, it is important to remember that this expansion is taking place and to relax into it with a sense of acceptance. Therefore, we find it a useful practice to include every thought or image that we sense during the meditation process as things that need to be there. We do not invalidate or fight them, and here's why. If we judge, fight and invalidate them as things that are not parts of ourselves and that should not be there, we defeat our purpose of centering on the zero-rest point. Negative judgement and invalidation requires negative energy, which puts a distance between us and the destination of our core vibratory energy. It takes longer to get there. Also, by fighting these thoughts and by trying to get rid of them, we give them more power. They are something we contain, and there is no place to dump them. The act of throwing them out just adds that much more energy to them, and when they hit our outer edge, they bounce back to us with equal force. We can however, acknowledge them and change them into thoughts we prefer. In the first place, they float into our awareness in meditation to let us know that we contain them. This way, if we see that they are not thoughts we prefer anymore, we can change them. Therefore, the presence of thoughts we judge as negative during the meditative process serves a positive purpose in letting us know that we are harboring them. The focus of this work is to point out that disease does exactly the same thing. After all, all tools are valid. It is necessary to enter the meditation process with an attitude of unconditional acceptance and curiosity. No struggle need be involved.

Depression is actually a type of meditation where we turn inwards to the self for answers we know are not available to us in our outer aware conscious reality. This is what occurs when depression is not judged as something negative or as an antisocial behavior. The depressed person allows himself to draw inwards and make changes in the belief, emotionality and thought components of himself. Therefore, when he emerges from this depression, he emerges as a changed person—a new personality. We in effect, center ourselves and alter our states of consciousness during depression as well as during meditation. It is only when the depressed state becomes a person's entire focus and prevents him from acting in a positive way within his environment that it ceases to serve a useful purpose.

Laughter also centers us and without invalidating depression, I consider laughter an ecstatically more enjoyable way to align with our core energy vibration. So, laugh and fill our world with your laughter.

13
Health Power: Making the Powerful More Powerful

The foundation of all human progress is man's realization that there is something more desirable than the condition in which he finds himself.

Take a good look at the condition in which you find yourself. Evaluate the circumstances of your life objectively and honestly. If you don't feel totally satisfied and totally excited about your life and what you are doing with it, you are not healthy, even if you are not physically ill. Recall that health is a condition of being in total alignment and in total harmony with the unique energy that one is. In this state, not only is there no disease, but one finds oneself creating and living the life of one's dreams. One's actions are directed towards making the individual the best possible human being he or she can be—in other words, the individual is achieving full self-expression. Satisfaction with life, wealth and happiness are by-products of living in total harmony with the energy that one is, which is the definition of living in health.

When you have achieved a measure of success in life, but feel that there's got to be something more to life, recognize that it is progress which is urging you to move on and experience the power that you are.

How does one go about experiencing the unique energy or power that one is? You can begin by fully becoming aware of what you are as a human being. The principles of metamedicine described in the first section of this book explain what the personality is. Understanding what the personality is basically composed of lets you see that there is nothing cast in concrete about who or what you are. You will begin to see and appreciate the fact that humans are malleable beings and that we can literally create ourselves to be whatever we want to be in this physical life.

"Well what does changing myself have to do with changing things in my life?" some people ask, after having forgotten portions of this book. As a review, please recall that it is the level of one's vibrational energy frequency that determines one's choice of actions in this life and consequently the type of life one experiences. Look at it this way. Everything is energy. What differentiates one thing from another is the differences in the vibratory frequency of their energies. What differentiates one reality in this world from another, such as a wealthy life versus a life of poverty, is the energy frequencies of people and events in each of these categories. Individuals who are positively aligned with their core energy frequency can only attract the positive frequency of a healthy and wealthy life. When it comes to human beings, the adage that opposites attract does not prove valid. Just as in achieving rapport where likes attract each other, so it is with human lives; one can only attract and experience a frequency similar to one's own frequency.

The easiest way to change one's life experience is to change the personality or the persona. Those who refuse to make changes in themselves and attempt to force changes in the outside world usually get intimately acquainted with struggle, conflict and pain. When they do reach their goals with this approach, they find no satisfaction or joy in victory. Perversely they often miss the struggle, which of course is the vibrational energy that they have become—constant wrangling. These are the individuals who are unhappy in what is judged to be a life of success and wealth.

The paradox of life in the physical world is that if you want to be healthy, happy and wealthy, you must first change your persona into that of a healthy, happy and wealthy person. Everything we want to see happen in our lives must of necessity begin with us and happen from us. The law of electromagnetic energy always remains valid because we are basically made out of electromagnetic energy. I will reiterate this law: whenever an electric force field is generated, a magnetic field or attraction force is created. Whenever we create a new image of ourselves by changing our blueprints in our belief systems, using sensory clarity of mentality and positive emotional energy, we generate electromagnetic energy. This energy creates a force field that attracts to us the things we desire or imagine.

What does it really take to change oneself? The most important element in human change is the willingness to take action. The only thing in physical life more important than this is possession of the physical life in the first place. So essential is the ability to take action that many times it is equated with having personal power. This desire to act, this personal power, is the foremost trait developed by all leaders and successful people.

With the willingness to act, one must then proceed to persistently make the changes in belief, emotion and thought that are necessary to create a new image of the self that one desires. Effecting these changes may require persistence but never struggle. Desire is the same energy as excitement; it lets you know that you will be in alignment with your unique vibratory energy frequency if you act *with integrity* on what it is you desire. Therefore, if your desire is to make changes in your persona, then no struggle, which is a negative energy, need be implied. Focus and persistence may be necessary, but struggle is never required. You may find that time and resources devoted to engaging the help of professionals experienced in the various skills of metamedicine will be worthwhile in providing you with great assistance in creating these changes.

Any changes made in the three aspects of the personality complex—belief, emotion and mentality—will change the self. You will not be the same person as you were before the change was made. An even more dumbfounding idea is that an individual's past and future can also be changed, as well as the present. In fact, you can systematically create your future and install it in your brain. This idea that time, the past, and the future can be manipulated, created and changed, is something our mentality finds difficult to accept. It must be experienced in order to appreciate its validity.

With the ability to take action and to change who we are at will, comes total control of our lives and our world. Wielding the power of health in this way will make the powerful infinitely more powerful.

Epilogue
Metamedicine and the Future

As we approach the end of this century, we look back with gratitude at the great advances in education, science, and medical technology. The advent of computer technology is changing the way we learn, and medical technology is prolonging our life span. Treatments and cures have been discovered for many illnesses, yet we still have disease.

Along with the advances in medicine have come many questions and dissatisfactions. The advances in medical technology have the effects of prompting people to expect even more miracles. "If doctors can cure all these diseases, why can't they keep us from getting sick in the first place?" people ask. Quality assurance controls, a euphemism for cost containment, are pressuring doctors and medical institutions to keep people well in the first place. Medical technology is expensive. Everybody wants it, but nobody is willing to pay for it. The doctors who are already under pressure to keep up with the latest in medical technology are caught in the middle of the medical finance war. They must meet the demand of the patients for the latest and best that medical technology has to offer and at the same time, face the accusations of driving up the cost of healthcare. The lawyers and the judicial system are watching from the sidelines, waiting to make a killing from the conflict. Our current health care climate is rife with distrust and fear. Forced to practice defensive medicine, many doctors find little joy and satisfaction in a profession which originally held great appeal as an opportunity to be of service in an intimately human way. Of course, the detached professionalism encouraged in medical schools and current medical establishments, as technology and specialization assumed greater importance, did very little to close the widening gap between the patient and the doctor.

The perceived detached attitude of the doctor and healthcare professionals is at the root of the patient's dissatisfaction with our current health care system. Every doctor needs to be a patient, as I have been, to understand the importance of trust in a doctor-patient relationship. When you are a patient, you are very vulnerable. You must depend on other people, especially the doctor, for your recovery and sometimes for your very life. To feel that your doctor truly cares for you, that she or he loves you, is one of the most important positive beliefs that pave the way for your recovery. Medicine is an intimately personal profession and when people sense that it is otherwise, it creates friction and unhappiness for all involved.

It becomes obvious as we enter the twenty-first century that we must change our thinking about health and medicine. Metamedicine redefines health and it brings the human consciousness factor into the practice of medicine, giving it infinitely wider scope and more power. With the understanding of the human conscious interplay in disease and health, medical science will truly begin to work miracles with or without expensive technology. Incurable diseases will become an obsolete concept.

The metamedicine approach to medical practice automatically creates a bond between the patient and the doctor that is almost lawyer-proof. Metamedicine teaches the patient self empowerment and allows the patient full responsibility for their lives and health. It restores to the patients their dignity and most importantly, it offers the patients an opportunity to use their disease as a step in the direction of a more desirable life.

Metamedicine holds the view that disease, like a mirror, reflects to us defects in our basic make up complex which we need to change in order to become the best possible human beings we are capable of being. Therefore, having gone through a disease, an individual will emerge better than he/she ever was prior to the illness. A doctor-healer who assists the patient in this endeavor will establish a relationship with this individual that transcends our current monetary economic considerations. The metamedicine practice invigorates the doctor-healer who approaches it with integrity. It would not be possible to practice metamedicine effectively in the absence of integrity. Again integrity means knowing that one is complete and powerful enough to get anything one desires without hurting anyone else or themselves in order to do so.

The doctor-patient relationship may continue in even more special ways long after the illness is over and here's why. The metamedicine encounter necessitated by the illness lets the patients perceive that they are just beginning to discover what they are and what life is about. These individuals will embark on a lifelong adventure of self-discovery and the doctor-patient relationship may wind up as the teacher-learner or friend-friend relationship. Doctors will have a very rewarding life if their patients become their lifelong friends.

When the entire staff of hospitals and other medical institutions are familiar with the metamedicine principles and approach to patient care, most of the current financial hassles and headaches will be over. Patients will recover much faster and be discharged from these institutions in a fraction of the time they do now.

Pursuit and achievement of the new definition of health as a much more expansive idea than the mere absence of disease will give us more powerful leadership in every field of endeavor: education, industry, business, government, research, and many other fields. With positive changes in the personalities of our leadership will come positive ideas that will create a more desirable world.

And what about disease? Will we still have disease? I don't know. I do know that metamedicine is teaching us to extract positive results from any disease. I believe that if our children are educated to know what they are as human beings and are taught to live life with integrity and self-empowerment, that disease will be a tool we will no longer need by the time the twenty-first century gets old.

As I stated at the beginning, the ideas contained in this work are new and yet, they are as old as humanity. All the concepts explored, all the methodologies and tools described, are intended as an introduction and as a catalyst to propel the reader's curiosity towards the journey of self-discovery and health. To have been of service in this way fills me with great joy and gratitude. Godspeed.

Glossary

Align - Positioning in parallel arrangement for movement in a common direction.

Anchor - A specific internal or external stimulus which, when connected to a set of responses, subsequently triggers the same responses when applied.

Anxiety - Generalized apprehension about a future event.

Association - Being fully inside a memory and looking through one's own eyes, hearing, feeling as if one was actually physically there. This is as opposed to being outside of the memory looking in and seeing oneself performing an action.

Attitude - A demonstration of a matrix of emotions and beliefs.

Balance - As in emotional balance: the zero rest point of all polarities of energy motion. The point from which motion in any direction is possible.

Behavior - Any activity engaged in by human beings in the physical world.

Belief - A thought pattern, conscious or unconscious, about an event or series of events in an individual's world. A perceived fact or truth.

Belief System - An individual's blueprint of what they experience in life. It is one aspect of the foundational structure of the human personality complex.

Compulsion - A compelling and undeniable motivation to engage in a certain behavior.

Communication - A process of transmitting information from one source to a target destination.

Confusion - The disorienting of the self from a rigidly held idea, in order to reorient oneself into a new direction. For example, the temporary state of disarray during formation of clearer ideas from a jumble of information.

Conscious Mind - The physiological awareness, which we consider to be the mentality. It is the part which focuses one to the physical world.

Creativity - The human act of expressing fully the unique energy one is in the world.

Deletion - The act of selectively paying attention to certain aspects of incoming sensory data that make up experience while leaving other sensory data out of that experience.

Disease - A *dis*-ease limitation in any aspect of the foundational aspects of the personality. It usually manifests physiologically as an illness.

Dissociation - The removal of the self from a previous perspective of something one has done in order to view the self from outside that perspective while still maintaining a model of the same perspective. As an example, looking at oneself in a picture so one does not have the feelings one would have in the actual event.

Distortion - The process of misrepresenting data in order to make shifts in the way we experience sensory data internally.

Ecstasy - The act of experiencing the total energy that one is.

Elicitation - The detection of certain internal processes by organized information gathering.

Emotion - Energy motion. The energy principle that activates belief systems into molding the personality's physical experience.

Eye Accessing Cues - The eye movements which are used to stimulate the brain to access the particular representational system with which one is processing information. They are catalysts which trigger appropriate areas of the brain to access pictures, sounds, and feelings.

Fear - Emotional energy associated with physical preservation of the self is positive fear. Negative fear is lack of willingness to acknowledge one's power.

Feeling - An external kinesthetic experience, such as touch, or internal kinesthetic experience, such as an evaluative response.

Focus - The fixating of attention to a particular idea which limits the awareness of all other ideas at a given time.

Hierarchy - Organization of ideas, which are given a ranking based on their relative importance.

Imagination - The space-time dimension in which we internally create and experience all ideas.

Integrity - The recognition that one is as powerful as one needs to be to get what one desires without forcing or harming others or oneself in order to do so.

Internal Representation - The coding of information created and stored in the mentality (thought) in the form of pictures, sounds, feelings, smells, and tastes.

Matching/Mirroring - Temporarily adopting another's behavior in order to achieve rapport with that person.

Model of the World - An individual's internal representation or organization of experience, which describes what one thinks the world is.

NLP - Neurolinguistic Programming. Neuro refers to the brain and nervous system and linguistic refers to language as it relates to the mind-experience.

Personality Construct - The representation of human consciousness in the world. It is made up of the hierarchy of belief, emotionality and thought, and it is unique to each individual.

Preference - The identification of that which one chooses without invalidation of things or ideas outside that choice.

Quark - The first level of solidification of vibratory patterns of energy into matter.

Rapport - The process of offering back another's behavior in such a way that trust is created. It is done with matching and mirroring behavior, as well as by empathy and love.

Reality - The idea of creation, which is being experienced, and in which one expresses one's life.

Reframe - Changing the meaning of an event, statement or word by changing the context.

Representational System - How we internally code sensory information perceived through the visual, auditory, kinesthetic, olfactory, and gustatory systems.

State - The sum total of the energy one expresses at any moment in time. One can be in a resourceful, positive state, or in an unresourceful, negative state.

Strategy - A sequence of internal representations that one engages to bring about a certain outcome. For example, there is a strategy for motivation, for decision, etc.

Submodalities - A subset or the finer distinctions of the modalities: visual, auditory, kinesthetic, olfactory, and gustatory. For example, the visual submodality may be brightness and color.

Thought - The third foundational aspect of the personality construct and that with which the self interacts with the world. Also called the "ego;" it forms a person's viewpoint of the world.

Time Line - A system for organization of memories in a linear time frame sequence, like the frames of a motion picture film.

Unconscious Mind - The portion of consciousness that is not in current mental awareness.

Appendix

*Take a good look at the condition in which you find
yourself. If you don't feel totally satisfied and totally
excited about your life and what you are doing with it,
you are not healthy, even if you are not physically ill.*
                                        Metamedicine.

M any people are excited about the metamedicine definition
of health as that state of human energy in which full self expression is possible. They desire the byproducts of health—satisfaction with life, wealth and happiness. Other people, on finding out
about metamedicine, bitterly complain that they have wasted their
lives in ill health and disease because they have lived in ignorance
of the power they are.

Please recognize that as long as you are alive, you have the
opportunity to acquire the skills which are necessary to achieve
health and create the life of your dreams.

Yes, it does take skill to give yourself, your relationships, and
your business the unique advantage of true health.

Metamed International provides training in health power skills
for three major groups of people: individuals, doctors and health
care professionals, and the U.S. industry.

If this work has touched a spark in you, take action now to
claim your birthright of health by putting into practice the fundamentals of metamedicine. We invite you to join us in the exploration of this exciting and rapidly evolving new technology in the field
of human health and empowerment. For more information on
books, seminars and training programs available, please detach and
mail the postcards enclosed.